Golden Highlights Library

Seashells Carson Ritchie

 Golden Press

Published in 1974 by **Golden Press, New York,**
a division of Western Publishing Company, Inc.
Library of Congress Catalog Card Number: 73–87969

Created, designed and produced for
Western Publishing Company, Inc. by
Trewin Copplestone Publishing Ltd, London

Printed in Italy by
Officine Grafiche Arnoldo Mondadori, Verona
Filmset by Photoprint Plates Ltd, Rayleigh, Essex
World rights reserved by
Western Publishing Company, Inc.
GOLDEN and GOLDEN PRESS ® are trademarks
of Western Publishing Company, Inc.

ISBN: 0 307 43116 9

Contents

Acknowledgments

The photographs for this book were taken by Michael
Dyer Associates except for those credited below to:
Heather Angel: 21b, 32t, b; Ashmolean Museum: 58,
71; Australian Tourist Commission: 74; BPC Picture
Library: 49b, 80; British Museum: 51, 64; Erwin
Christian: 40; Hamlyn Group: 65; Michael Holford:
12, 56b, 61bl; Det Kongelige Biblioteck, Copenhagen:
70b; Mansell Collection: 62–3, 66, 75, 78; Natural
History Museum, London: 31, 44, 52b; Dr Carson
Ritchie: 68b; Shell Photographic Division: 63b;
Transworld Feature Syndication: 76, 77, 79; Victoria
and Albert Museum: 57t; Wallace Collection: 67.
The publishers would like to thank the Horniman
Museum and Library, London, for making available
for photography the subjects illustrated on pages 47 and
48(b).

Page 1 *Tun shells (Dolium variegatum). The
ridges on these shells give them strength to support
the battering of tropic seas.*

The precious wentletrap was once such a rare collector's item that unscrupulous dealers forged it in rice paste.

The Lure of Shells

SHELLS have exerted a fascination over man for many thousands of years. When you pick up a shell from the beach and take it carefully home you join only the most recent of many generations stretching back into prehistory who have been attracted by their shapes and colors.

Cave dwellers of the New Stone Age living in Hundsteig, in Austria, collected shells and strung them into necklaces to keep them safe and make them easily portable. The necklaces they made included shells of the snails *Melanopsis vindobonensis* and *Cyclonasa neritea,* the conch *Lythoglyphus naticoides* and many other decorative shells including the fossil *Cerithium.*

Aristotle was probably the first person to keep a scientific shell collection. In Roman times two consuls are known to have been collectors, and a hoard of exotic shells was found among the ruins of excavated Pompeii.

In our own age Hirohito, the Emperor of Japan, was such an enthusiastic collector that he designated a species of large cone shell *(Pleurotomaria salmiana)* an "Imperial Treasure", and anyone who exported it from Japan did so at peril of his life. The author Ian Fleming was

another shell enthusiast, and was probably much happier collecting shells in Jamaica than when working on his James Bond thrillers.

Enthusiasm for shells can become obsessive. In the South Sea islands chiefs waged bloody battles against their neighbors for the possession of a single highly valued cone shell, and the islanders of the New Hebrides would cut a ton of sandalwood to trade for just one violet-lipped cowrie *(Ovulum angulosum).*

It is not difficult to see why people become so excited about shells. Nature lacks nothing as designer or as craftsman. The elegant convolutions of the nautilus shell, with its marvelously connected chambers, make the same appeal to the eye as does the spiral staircase of a Georgian mansion. On each occasion Nature reproduces every detail of her grand conception with a complexity that man can never match. Yet each individual has its differences and each shell is unique. It is impossible for anyone to withhold their admiration for a lovely shell like the *Guildfordia triumphans* or the *Ranella pustulosa,* for either certainly equals if not exceeds in beauty anything that could be made by man.

Shells have a powerful mystery. However lovely, they are not art objects–they are the

3

Murex cabritii (above), *from the Florida beaches and* (below) Cantharidus opalus *from New Zealand.*

remains of a once vital organism, a creature that seems to have left little trace in his deserted home. What was the animal like that made the empty shell on the collector's shelf? What deep sea or distant shore did it inhabit? How did its complex patterns come into being?

The more one studies shells, the more the sense of mystery grows. Take the colors of shells for example. Although the pigments, such as porphyrin, used in creating the brilliant colors of shells have been painstakingly analyzed, scientists have so far failed to produce a really convincing reason why shells should be colored at all.

The world of shells is full of strange and lovely things such as the nautilus, which can change its buoyancy by altering the density of the gas it carries in its chambers. As a result it rises and descends in the ocean depths at will, like a submarine balloon, and all without its shell being shattered—a shell that is so fragile that if it once drops to the ground it is almost sure to break.

Shell collecting offers a great many unique advantages that are not associated with other forms of collecting. It is infinitely extendable. There are so many different types of shells that you will never run short of something to collect. It is also a very economical hobby to pursue. The top price paid for even a rare shell is a long way from that paid for a painting, a piece of fine porcelain, or even a rare stamp. Nor need a collector pay anything for his treasures unless he wants to: some enthusiasts never collect anything they have not found themselves.

Seashells need no special care for their conservation and do not decay or deteriorate. Most of them are practically indestructible. (Land species are much more fragile.)

In 1855, when Charles Kingsley published *Glaucus or the Wonders of the Shore*, he felt he had to write an elaborate apology, defending shell collecting and other natural history pursuits from the prejudices that people had about them. Such a defense is no longer necessary—though Kingsley still makes very interesting reading—because shell collecting has established itself as a popular hobby in the intervening century and a quarter.

Today shell collectors come from all walks of society, from the ordinary citizen to people of high position. It is a hobby that demands neither wealth nor great erudition but can easily be carried on by the ordinary person with a few cents to spend or the time to investigate the treasures of the tideline.

A shell from Hong Kong, Guildfordia triumphans, *which exhibits the phenomenon of golden iridescence.*

Murex beaui (right), *a rare shell from Cuba,*
and (left) Murex tenuispina–*"thin-spined"–*
from the Ryuku islands.

The World of Shellfish

STRICTLY speaking, the creatures that inhabit the shells coveted by collectors are not shellfish but the group of animals known as mollusks. Conchologists, who study the shells themselves, and malacologists–biologists who are more interested in the animal contained in the shell than the container–feel that the word "shellfish" should be kept to designate crabs, lobsters and other crustaceans, and even they, of course, are not fish.

What is a mollusk? The word itself comes from the Latin *mollis* meaning "soft." All mollusks have soft bodies, including the garden slug, which is a mollusk that has lost its shell. However, what we most often associate with the mollusks is their hardness–the hardness of the stony envelopes that enclose them while they lie buried in the mud, or that they carry around on their backs. These shell coverings are a form of stone, just as are mountains and cliffs. They are made from the same ingredients that constitute the terrestrial mineral aragonite, or the marine gem, precious coral. In fact, recognizing shells for what they are, jewels of the sea, will help to give an understanding of their nature.

It seems a paradox that some of the most advanced mollusks, the land and sea slugs and the octopus, have no shells. Others, such as the squid and cuttlefish, have an internal shell that only becomes visible when the creature has died and its body has decomposed. Members of the mollusk group or *phylum* which have learned how to do without shells altogether are the nudibranchs or "naked gill" shellfish. Many of them are extremely beautiful, but this beauty disappears when they die, while the shells of their humbler relatives retain their shape and color.

It would be a mistake to imagine that everything that lives in the sea and secretes a hard shell is a mollusk. Precious coral, which grows hard, gem-like bushes of such varied and attractive colors–red, white, pink, and so forth–is a collection of marine polyps. Sea-urchins have a hard, shell-like structure but they are not related to mollusks, and the shape of their hard bodies is much more complex than that of a mollusk, which usually has a simple one-piece, or hinging two-piece shell, the valves, or two halves, of which are often symmetrical.

Nor is everything soft that crawls along the bottom of the sea necessarily a mollusk. Among the slug-like creatures, for example, is the famous *bêche de mer,* that aristocrat of Chinese menus, which is not a slug, but a sea cucumber.

It is often difficult, even for a malacologist, to determine just what is and what is not a mollusk. As in other cases where paternity is disputed, a blood test is called for to settle the matter. Comparison of their blood groups has determined that mollusks are more closely related to segmented worms, or *annelids*, than to other living creatures. Both families have been found to have spirally separated blood cells, a characteristic of all mollusks. Another way in which a creature that may not seem like a mollusk can be identified as one is by examining the way in which its offspring develop. Many mollusks go through a larval stage, and creatures which seem as unlike other shellfish as possible, such as winged sea butterflies (heteropods), can nevertheless be recognized as mollusks simply because their full-grown shape is exactly like that of a mollusk *veliger* larva.

There are probably 100,000 different species of mollusks, and 50,000 of them live in the sea. In this vast number there is room for infinite variation. Because they differ so much from each other there is no such thing as a typical mollusk that all the others resemble. But it is possible to construct an imaginary mollusk of whose features every member of the groups will possess some. It has a shell that serves as a substitute for a backbone. The shell is much more a skeleton than a house, because many mollusks, even though they have shells, like to find homes or construct burrows for themselves. The piddock, for example, digs a tunnel into solid gneiss, a granite-like rock. The average mollusk has a soft body containing its main organs enveloped in a thin mantle, or *epithelium*, which secretes the shell, if one exists. In a cavity beneath the mantle there will be gills, unless the mollusk has adapted itself to breathe air direct, in which case gills are replaced by a kind of lung. There will also be some kind of foot, a muscular appendage which in mollusks with one-piece shells (univalves) will be an oval or rounded disc, and in those with two-piece shells (bivalves) will be triangular or hatchet-shaped.

Mollusks have a complex nervous system, a heart, kidneys and, usually, a stomach which connects with a mouth, and an anus. Reproduction is usually sexual but the pattern varies between male, female, bisexual and hermaphroditic mollusks. In more highly developed mollusks there is a definite head, and the

A plate from Charles Kingsley's Glaucus, showing a hermit crab and a periwinkle shell, and (inset, top left), *the queen conch (Strombus gigas), found off Florida and the West Indies, from which divers obtain pink pearls. It is also used for carving cameos (see page 59).*

Above *A group of chiton, or coat-of-mail, shells, creatures very close to the primeval mollusk.*

Below *A plate from Kingsley's* Glaucus, *showing a* Turritella (left) *and a* Littorina littorea (right).

mouth is equipped with a distinct feeding organ called a *radula*. This is carried on a band of muscle known as the *odontophore*. It is a horny, ribbon-like tongue, shaped rather like an elephant's trunk, which is armed with a set of rasping files. The radula can develop into some extraordinary forms, from the masonry drill of the piddocks to a deadly sting in the group of cone shells called *Toxoglossa*, which use it to inject poison into their victims.

Some mollusks have eyes, and in advanced forms there may be tentacles or antennae-like feelers. The octopus, which is shell-less, has the most highly developed eyes of all the mollusks, but if a screen is set up on the bed of an aquarium the octopus will not try to swim around it until after investigating with its tentacles.

It must be clear from even this brief attempt to describe a typical mollusk that their variations are so great that the task is almost impossible. Indeed the mollusk features that a particular species exhibits may be totally lacking in one of its relatives. Mollusks may vary in size from as tiny as a pin's head to sixty feet in length. They may be carnivorous and cannibalistic or may filter food particles from the water. They may swim with jet-propelled ease or anchor themselves immovably to rocks. Yet, in spite of all this great variety, there are two species often mistaken for mollusks that actually belong to other families. The lamp shells, or brachiopods, which look like bivalve mollusks, are survivors of another very ancient phylum, and the barnacles, though once thought to be mollusks, in fact are members of the family of arthropods.

The Six Families

THE mollusks form the second largest group in the animal kingdom (the arthropoda form the largest) and the many species within it can be divided into six main branches or classes. Until 1957 it was thought that there were only five, but in that year biologists were surprised to discover a missing member.

During 1950–52 a Danish research expedition under the direction of Dr Henning Lemche carried out dredging operations in some of the deepest-known parts of the oceans. On May 6, 1952, its research ship *Galathea* was trawling off the west coast of Central America at a depth of 1945 fathoms (more than 2 miles) when it brought up a number of mollusks that were thought to be a kind of limpet—they were just under an inch in diameter, with a thin flattened shell. Like all the other samples collected they were preserved for later investigation. Not until five years later was it established that ten specimens and three empty shells of this limpet-like creature, now named *Neopilina galatheae*, were in fact a species of mollusk type thought to have become extinct in Devonian times, 350 million years ago.

Careful examination of this "living fossil" revealed features that were different from those of all other known mollusks. It had previously been known from fossil examples that this was a member of the monoplacophora. Now, this most primitive of all the living mollusks revealed a segmented structure to the body, suggesting a link with the annelid worms rather than with the flatworm that had previously been thought the mollusk's ancestor. This implied that the mollusk branched off from its evolutionary line at a higher level than had been thought.

Neopilina has a body composed of repeating parts with a head and tail outside the series. There are eight pairs of muscles to retract the foot, ten pairs of nerves radiating to the sides of the foot, and five pairs each of gills and excretory organs. The head is well defined but it has no eyes. There is a mouth on the underside with a radula and broad tentacles around the lips. Other specimens have since been found, all off the Pacific coast of America within fifteen degrees of the equator, but this remains the only known species, although other shells with the segmented structure of this primeval limpet will doubtless be found.

After the monoplacophora the earliest group of mollusks is the loricata, also known as the amphineura or chitons. As the last name implies, the best-known species of this family are the chiton or coat-of-mail shells. These mollusks, which have eight overlapping plates or valves, look somewhat like the woodlice of the insect world. The body is symmetrical and shows some trace of segmented development in its ancestry but this is not associated with the arrangement of the plates. The plates are linked by a tough leathery girdle which sometimes carries tuft- or spine-like excrescences. Sometimes the plates provide a real coat of armor for the chiton but often they are proportionately small for the size of the animal and form a row of separate plates that offer little or no protection along the center of the chiton's back. The girdle and its decoration is often more colorful than the valves, but the shell is sometimes elaborately patterned. Occasional abnormal forms are found with six, seven or nine valves. Unlike most other mollusks the chitons have a mouth at one end of the body and an anus at the other. They have a radula but no tentacles and no eyes. They can creep about on their feet but spend most of the time on or under the rocks and stones of the intertidal shore. Many of the 600 species have light-sensitive organs in their shells, a feature unique to this group.

The mussel (Mytilus edulis), *one of the best-known bivalves, is also a gourmet's delight.*

The gastropods are everyone's idea of a shellfish. The snail is the best-known member of the family. There are about 40,000 species of marine gastropods, and they make a strong claim to being the most colorful and the most excitingly shaped of all marine shells. The gastropods are univalves, that is, they have only one shell, which sits on top of them like an upturned trash-can.

Gastropods have acquired a strong bias towards the right from their earliest years, although a few do coil to the left and some land species may coil in either way. When they are at the larval veliger stage their bodies begin to spiral, and as they start to build their shells these spiral too, so that most gastropods have coiled or spiraled shells. Their bodies twist through half a turn so that they are bent into the position of someone who is always touching his toes, bringing their excretory and reproductive organs next to their heads.

On the sole of their foot the gastropods secrete a second piece of shell that they can use to close the aperture in their main shell after the body has been drawn inside. This shiny

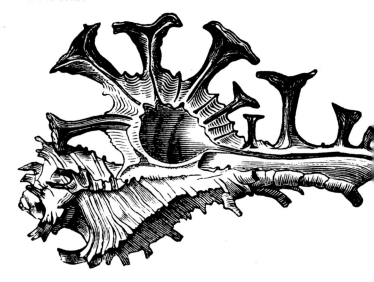

round secondary shell, called the *operculum*, once puzzled malacologists, who thought that it was the part of the gastropods which corresponded to their twin-shelled cousin's second shell. However, it is now thought to be merely a special protective device in certain species. It may also be used as a hook to help the foot of the mollusk claw its way along as it moves forward with an undulating rolling action.

Once shut in, with its operculum closed, the shellfish is relatively safe from attack. Opercula, which are often found on the beach separated from their parent shell, are much prized not merely by collectors but for jewelry. They can be ear-shaped, such as those belonging to *Polinices* and *Lunatia*, both forms of moon snails, but are more usually round. Many of these opercula have familiar names, such as "cat's eye" the name of the operculum of the tapestry turban *(Turbo petholatus)*.

Torsion has compressed the organs of gastropods so that some species have partially or completely reduced those which they once owned on the right side of the body, including the gill *(ctenidium)* and its auricle, and the right kidney. I mention this point because the spirally coiled shell, so attractive to collectors, may be one of Nature's mistakes. In most species shells which coil in the "wrong" direction are so rare as to be choice collector's items.

Most gastropods have a well-developed head, with sense organs, a radula in the mouth, and a foot suited for steady rather than speedy progress. The great scientist William Beebe studied a periwinkle crawling across his desk top and across the manuscript of a book that he was writing and found that it could crawl at the rate of three inches in a minute. Moreover it could maintain this speed no matter which surface it was moving over. Which of us could maintain such a consistent pace over ground which kept on changing its nature? Gastropods are extremely tenacious of life, the best-known example of this tenacity being a (land) snail which was collected in Egypt, brought back to the British Museum, and showed signs of life after having been stuck down on a card for four years.

Some gastropods, such as most of the opisthobranchia or sea slugs, have abandoned their shell and mantle altogether. Others are fast, open-sea swimmers like the heteropods (sea butterflies), which have fragile and trans-

The best-known of all univalves is the Helix aspera, *or common snail.*

parent shells if they have shells at all, and the pteropods, which swim with flipper-like extensions of the foot.

Tusk shells or scaphopods, numbering about 200 species, sometimes look like tiny colorless cucumbers, but most are shaped just like an elephant's tusk with the tip broken off. They have neither head nor eyes and breathe through their mantles, having done away with their gills, and have a body specially designed for their form of life. A broad foot pushes into the mud with a powerful radula, which has tentacles to pick up food fragments. Scaphopods live in both deep and shallow water.

Bivalves or double shells, as opposed to the single-shelled univalves, are called lamellibranchs in Europe and pelecypods in America. The first name refers to their plate-shaped gills, the second to the "hatchet foot" on which they creep. There are more than 5000 marine species. Oysters, mussels, cockles, and scallops are all typical pelecypods. The two valves of the shell are usually similar. They are hinged by means of an integument and kept closed by a powerful muscle, and by teeth along the edge of the shell. Bivalves can propel themselves by jet propulsion, crawl, or even hop on their foot. Some pelecypods lash themselves to a rock with a *byssus* or threadlike mooring rope. Others use their foot to dig into sand or mud. Most lamellibranchs feed on minute fragments of detritus carried to them by the currents. They have no real head and lack eyes, tentacles or radula, but their gills collect the food fragments and filter them into their stomach.

Of all the mollusks, the cephalopod family has achieved the most sophisticated development, and is the most intelligent. Some have the ability to change color to match their surroundings, and during mating the male is known to blush. There are upwards of 800 species, but probably they have not yet all been discovered for they include the giant squids—the kraken or sea monsters of sailors' tales—about which very little is known. They are active, free-swimming predators who jet their way through the sea by emitting water through a siphon.

The cephalopods are perhaps most easily recognized by their eight to ten prehensile arms, familiarly known as tentacles, which they use to catch and hold their prey. Some have interior shells, like the cuttlefish and the spirula, but most have none, like the octopus, the best-known species in the group.

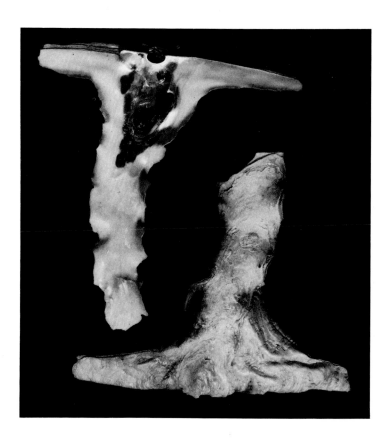

The Shape of Shells

THE shapely forms of the hard exterior container of mollusks which, with the glowing colors of the shells, form their chief attraction to the collector, are to a large extent determined by the area of the sea in which the animal lives and on its way of life.

Those species that live far from land, out in the open sea or in the ocean deeps, are not constantly battered against hard rocks and do not need thick protective shells. When they float near the surface they may have thin, transparent shells so that a bird, looking down on them, will think that they are jellyfish. Helmet shells, on the other hand, exposed to the battering of the surf on coral reefs, need all the protection they can get, while the aggressive nature and the fighting qualities of the queen conch have resulted in its acquiring the heaviest and thickest armor-plating enjoyed by any moving shell. Not just the thickness, but the shape of a shell, is determined in part by the animal's habitat. The helmet shells, which I have just mentioned, have an additional protection of knobs and ridges. Limpets, which have to stand up to a lot of punishment, have fluted shells, with ridged hollows running down to the edge of the shell from its center. These flutes give them double the strength that a shell of a plane surface would have, just

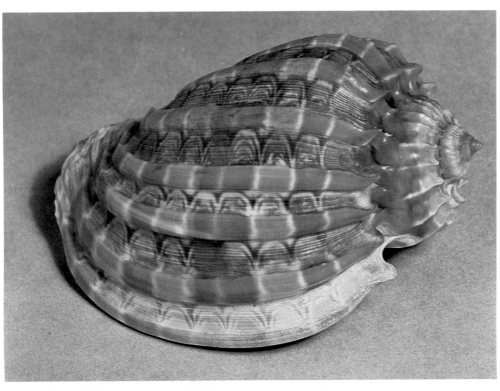

Left *The harp shell (Harpa ventricosa) owes its bright coloring to the warm tropical water in which it lives.*

Right *The Pacific triton shell (Charonia tritonis) frequently grows to a length of fifteen inches. These shells are often used as trumpets.*

Below *The baler shell, a native of the Great Barrier Reef, is used by the Pacific islanders as a container, cooking pot and drinking vessel.*

as corrugated iron is twice as strong as a flat plate of metal.

Shellfish which are exposed to pounding from the seas often have a streamlined shape, like a shallow cone. Top shells, purple shells, periwinkles, and limpets all have this characteristic form.

The knobs and corrugations on a shell's surface can have a purpose other than providing extra strength. They can be intended to stop the shell being swept too far from its original station by a wave, by arresting it like the flukes of an anchor. They also serve as a support for a camouflage of marine growths which will cover the shell and render it invisible as it moves along the bottom of the sea. Shells like the queen conch have strong upstanding projections around which weeds can wrap themselves. The queen conch also has a very rough exterior surface, something which favors the growth of marine algae.

Heavy shells provide a wonderful protection against the stony palate teeth of fish, but the weight is a burden. By continually thickening its shell from inside as it gets older, a shellfish is cutting down on its mobility. Old shellfish, with really heavy shells, wander a lot less than young shellfish with light ones. Moreover the older and heavier a shellfish becomes the more likely it is to be attacked by small boring worms and other parasites. This is particularly true of the pearl oyster *(Meleagrina margaritifera)*. Once a shell valve has grown to more than a pound and a quarter in weight, it has been riddled by so many worm holes that it is rejected as "scabby" by pearl button makers.

Although every shellfish tries to build its archetypal design, laid down millions of years ago by evolutionary process, shellfish, like other beings, have to cut their coat according to their cloth. The quantity and quality of minerals available to them may not be right to build just the shell they would like. I have always been forcibly struck by this fact while looking through cameo shells to find specimens with a good strong color in their middle layer. Time and time again I found that the middle layer of a shell was rather colorless and not a deep brown. So the quantity of lime which a shell can assimilate governs its shape and thickness to some extent. Areas where no lime at all is to be had rarely produce shellfish. This can be seen much more readily on land than on sea, by making a count of the number of snails on particular areas associated with a particular geological pattern. On clay bottoms,

Trisidos tortuosum, one of the strangest-shaped of all tropical shells.

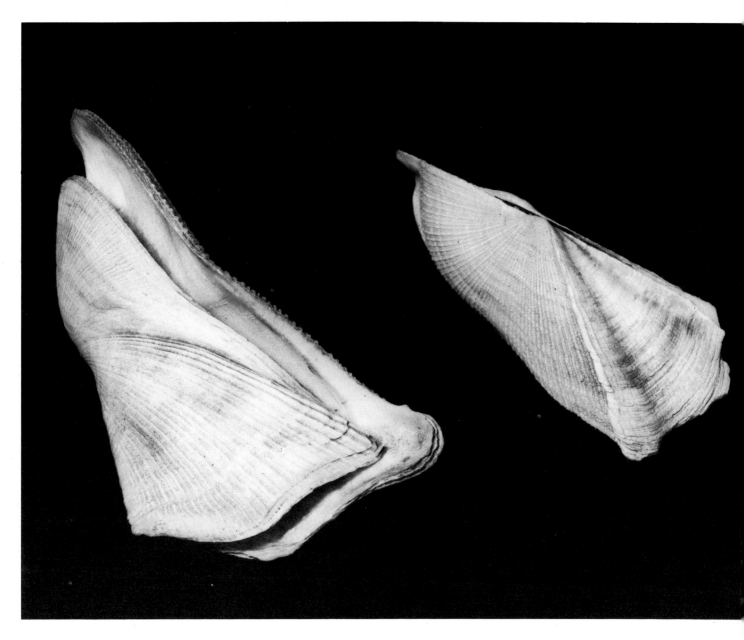

or deep, undisturbed water, thin shells tend to be the rule. Areas where there is a lot of lime available, such as coral reefs, tend to favor species with very heavy shells, such as the helmet shells.

What is going to be the end result of all this calcium carbonate constantly drawn from the water of the sea by shellfish? Much of it, of course, returns to other animal life by the adsorption of small species of shellfish by other sea creatures. The shells of dead shellfish are ground to sand by the action of the sea in tidal waters. One of the most striking features of shells, however, is their permanence. They are being laid down on the sea bottom in layers which may one day rise above the sea like the chalk cliffs of southern England, built up in Cretaceous times.

The Color of Shells

NOT all shells are colored. Internal shells and those of species from the lightless ocean depths usually have either no color or very little. Fully grown shells have attained their full color, young and immature ones often lack it. Sick shells will change to a dull bluish black.

Climate has a major effect on shell colors. A French naturalist once remarked: "The shell is a medal struck by Nature to commemorate climates." The change in color of shells even of the same species from one part of the world to another can be seen in spectacular fashion in the pearl oyster. What pearl-shell dealers call "white mop" (MOP = mother-of-pearl) is characteristic of Australian waters, the Celebes,

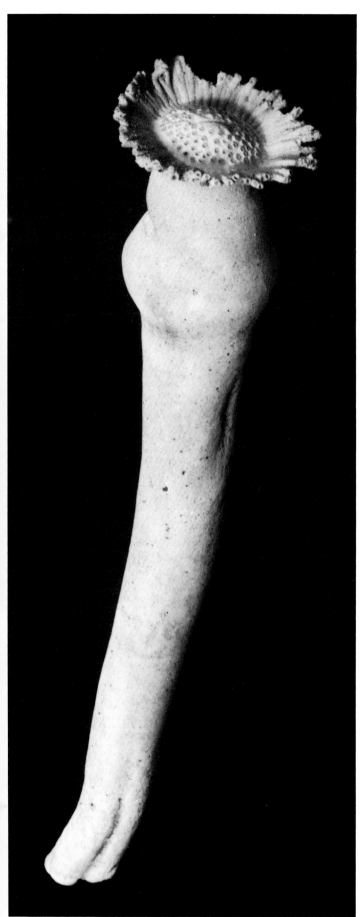

Brechites radix, *from the Torres Strait, is an example of a shell which has assumed a vegetable form.*

The chambered nautilus has a zebra-striped brown and cream shell which was utilized by the Dutch shell carvers to cut cameos.

Borneo, Macassar and Arawi Island, though even in this area there are variations in the colors of the white. As the shell beds get nearer to the equator the famous "gold lip" nacre makes its appearance, a warm amber-colored tone, seen at its best in the shells from the Philippines. Then around Tahiti and the Cook Islands, the nacre turns to a smoky dark color, the equally famous "black lip." What causes these color changes? Pearl-shell dealers are convinced that the food available for the oyster in different areas is the principal factor, and this certainly seems to be borne out by investigations undertaken in British waters. There whelks, fed on barnacles, were found to develop white shells, while whelks feeding on mussels developed dark or pink shells. Food is not the only factor, however: the amount of sunlight available and the temperature of the water are other potent forces.

The color of shells is not superficial but an integral part of the shell, although it may sometimes be confined to the periostracum. Pigment is secreted by special glands situated only at the front of the mantle and once incorporated into the shell is not altered in any way by the mollusk. Continuously active color cells deposit unbroken masses of color, such as stripes that run right down the side of a shell. Intermittently acting color glands produce spots and patches of irregular form.

Why are shells colored? There seems to be no single, convincing answer to this question. Some colored shellfish may use their colors to attract mollusks of the opposite sex, but then some shellfish are both sexes at once and so hardly need this attractive power. In any case

Below *The purple sea snail has a two-colored shell which makes it appear like foam from below and like jellyfish from above.*

Right *The thorny oyster gave its glowing reds to the Aztec mosaics. It was so precious that even worm-eaten specimens were used.*

the foot or mantle of the animal is often much more colorful than the shell itself. The mantle of the giant clam (*Tridacna gigas*) is not only brightly colored but is covered with specks of transparent tissue called hyaline organs which focus the bright sunlight in the shallow waters of the reefs where these clams are found. The light is concentrated onto the large numbers of an algae called *Zooxanthellae*, facilitating the photosynthesis by which they build their tissue. The clam feeds on this algae, so may be said to farm its own food upon its mantle.

Some shells are deep divers, such as the nautilus. The nautilus is essentially an abyssal shellfish and one would have thought that the colorful effect of its zebra-striped brown and cream shell would have been entirely lost on other nautili in the darkness of the ocean deeps in which it lives. In darkness there can be no color because all color comes from light. The brilliant colors of the cowries are never seen during the animal's lifetime; they are permanently covered by a mantle which spreads over the shell. Traces of where the edges joined can frequently be seen as a slight

ridge on the upper surface of a cowrie shell. Similarly the beautiful iridescence of nacre, such as that shown in the silvery chambers of the nautilus, was never intended to be seen at all.

It is a sobering thought that the coloring of shells may be merely a way of disposing permanently of harmful body chemicals, such as porphyrin. There is a human analogy in the disease called porphyria, from which George III of England is thought to have suffered. The body toxins which cause the pain associated with this incurable disease are akin to porphyrin. They are eliminated in the urine of the patient, and color it a bright purple.

Another explanation of color in shells is that it is intended to signal to possible predators that the shellfish in question is inedible. *Janthina janthina,* a sea snail which travels along on a raft of bubbles trapped by mucus, is a classic instance. Its shell is purple on top, lilac color below. Seen from below by a fish, the *Janthina janthina,* surrounded by its raft of air-bubbles, looks like a floating patch of seafoam, from which no nourishment is to be derived. Seen

from above, its purple top appears to birds to be that of an inedible and poisonous jellyfish.

Many color schemes are probably intended for camouflage, and when a shell has conspicuous coloring provision is sometimes made to prevent its brilliance from alerting predators. Thus the vibrant red thorny oyster *(Spondyl aurantium)* is covered with prickly spines. These are obviously intended to attract marine plants, which will live on the oyster's back and camouflage it completely.

Some shells can even change color to blend in with a new environment. This is the case with the blue-rayed limpet *(Helcion)*. When young it is to be found near the surface on the broad fronds of large tangles of oar-weed. These fronds are purple-brown in color, and to prevent it from being seen as it climbs on them the blue-rayed limpet carries a brown shell with three to six lines of bright blue radiating from the apex and giving an iridescent gleam similar to that which is seen on the tangles. As it gets older the limpet climbs down the stem and attaches itself to the suckers with which the weed clings to the rock. There

The blue bands on the shell of the blue-rayed limpet fade during the change from infant to adult life, when it changes its habitat.

is no iridescence there and so the blue lines on its shell gradually become obscured by new layers until it blends in completely with the stems of the weed. In youth the shell is thin, but as it moves down the weed the shape is modified so that it can cling to the round stem of the weed, instead of the flat surface of the frond, and the shell thickens considerably because it will now take much more battering from the sea.

The octopus, although it does not have a shell, is more highly developed than other mollusks, not least in its control of color. Laymen and scientists alike are fascinated by its chameleon-like ability to change color in as little as two thirds of a second. The special pigment cells called chromatophores on the octopus' body can expand to sixty times their contracted size, thus painting the body of the animal in the color desired and in the pattern selected by the central nervous system, which controls these color changes. Octopuses placed in tanks with a floor of black and white squares have induced similar colors in their chromatophores.

An octopus will change color as it swims over the bottom of the sea, turning brown to match the rock, grey for coral, yellow for sand and green for weeds. If it settles down it will induce a two-colored pattern of light and dark spots, to help it blend in with the background and throw some sand over its body to ensure complete camouflage.

The Substance of Shells

IT is not often realized that shells contain two absolutely unique substances. One of them is the porcelaneous material which constitutes heavy shells such as clams, the other is the iridescent nacre, or mother-of-pearl, which lines shells such as pearl oysters and abalones. The porcelaneous type of shell almost certainly suggested the invention of porcelain by the Chinese. Although the horny covering of some shells does not have as remarkable an appearance as the nacre, it has played a very important part in history because shells were one of the hardest substances known to early peoples, much harder than iron or bronze for example. The horny type of shell was used for a great variety of cutting purposes and for carving hard stones such as jade.

The nacre is the most unusual and remark-

Below *The carrier shell is the original shell collector. In spite of its accumulated spoil it is very active.*

Bottom *Star shells, such as these, protect themselves by closing their operculum (see the specimen on the left).*

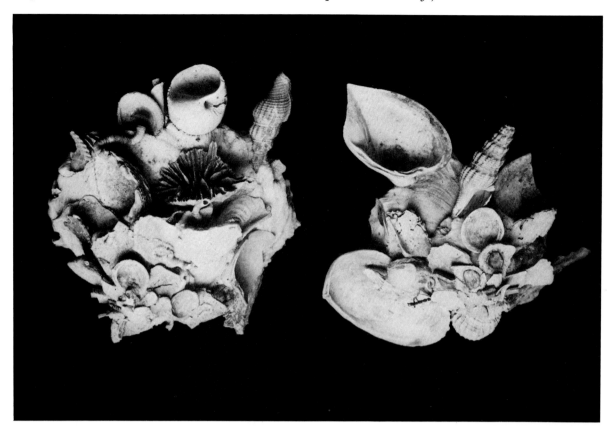

The conches are among the fiercest of shellfish, though the three shown here look deceptively pretty, with their curves and delicate colors.

able of all shell substances. It has been imitated, unsuccessfully, for hundreds of years. However, some clues to its nature became available when the British scientist Sir David Brewster showed that the iridescence of nacre was due to its surface shape. This led to moderately successful attempts being made to produce iridescence in other materials such as steel by shaping them in a similar way. Although the substance of shells is chemically very close to that of the terrestrial mineral aragonite, their composition is such that they have a distinctive beauty which is entirely their own.

The fabric of shells is made up mainly of calcium carbonate, with a small proportion of calcium phosphate, and minute amounts of magnesium carbonate and silica. It is the balance of these different ingredients in the mixture that distinguishes the composition of seashells from that of crabs or shrimps. A lobster shell, for example, contains about 15 per cent of calcium phosphate mixed with the calcium carbonate. This makes it quite fragile —we can crunch up shrimps with our teeth, whereas no one would think of eating a winkle, the shell of which contains a high proportion of calcium carbonate, and little

calcium phosphate, except by removing the animal from its shell with a pin. It is the high percentage of calcium carbonate which produces the glassy porcelaneous surfaces or shimmering nacre ones which have already been mentioned.

The process whereby a mollusk, by definition one of the softest of animals, produces shell, one of the hardest substances known to man, is one of Nature's miracles. Of course the process is a long-drawn-out affair. In most species, and particularly in bivalves, the inner surface of the mantle is lined with minute hairs *(cilia)* that help to create water currents. A mollusk ingurgitates and filters out a very large quantity of water during its lifetime—as much as thirty or forty gallons a day in the case of some lamellibranchs. The mollusks' efficient filtrage system is much more productive than anything man has been able to devise.

Once extracted from the seawater the minerals required for shell-building are deposited, by means of the mantle, onto a framework of conchiolin, an animal substance, which forms as it were a mold for the deposition of the carbonates. Making cement that will harden under water is just another of the

Below *Iridescence is common to all nacreous shells, such as the chambered nautilus (left) and the pearl oyster (right).*

Bottom *Miniature metal figures of Buddha (left) in a mussel, and (right) a fish trapped in an oyster shell, both covered by layers of nacre.*

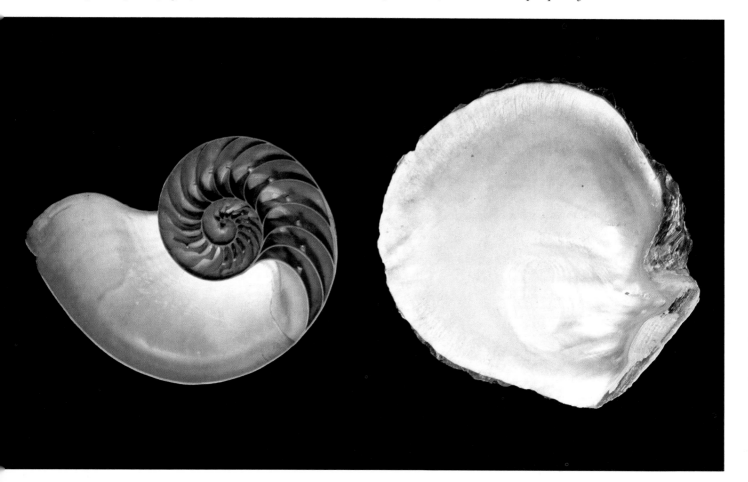

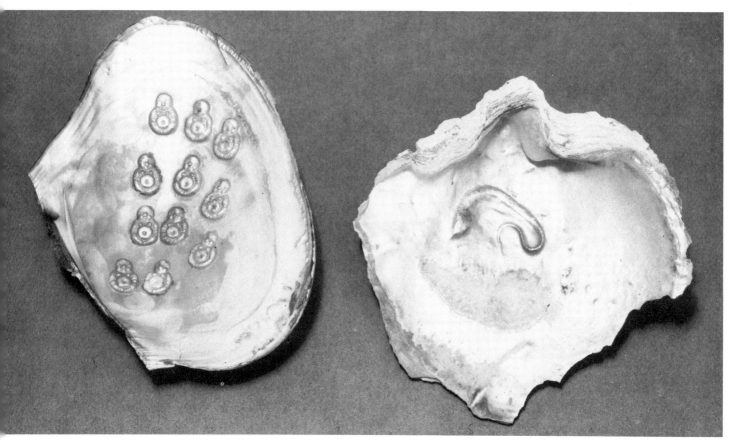

clever tricks which mollusks have learned during the evolutionary process. Conchiolin is continually applied to the shell by the shellfish, and keeps its home in good condition, just like an occasional coat of paint. When the animal dies, the supplies of conchiolin cease. What has been applied begins to disintegrate, and the empty shell becomes more brittle as time passes. Of course this is much less noticeable in the robust shells of marine shellfish than in their terrestrial relatives. However, one other benefit of applications of conchiolin is that it preserves the color and gloss of shells. Probably it is owing to lack of conchiolin that the colors of some shells fade in the sun, such as those of queen conch. Cameos and pearls from this conch also fade. The iridescence of mother-of-pearl also dies if it is exposed to the sun—a fact that is well known to shell merchants, but not to museum curators who expose irreplaceable treasures of nacre to the sun in glass cases. Although natives of Borneo have long known that the jewelry that they make from hornbill ivory will retain its natural color only if it is rubbed with oil milked from the uropygial gland in the rump of the bird, shell collectors have not so far tried to obtain, or synthesize conchiolin to treat their treasures. Nevertheless it is an obvious step to take.

The laying down of the shell is carried out mainly by the margin of the mantle, though in some species the foot is also capable of secreting shell layers. The mantle pushes out past the edge of the shell, depositing a calcareous mixture on it and building it up year by year as the shellfish grows outwards. Layers of material, and a thickened outside rim of the shell, indicate age, and the number of distinct segments in the layer, seen in a cross section cut through it, can enable one to make a guess at the age of the shellfish, just like the rings in a tree. Only the edge of the mantle produces color and pattern on a shell's surface.

The outer edge of the typical mantle is composed of two or three lobes that each lay down one of the layers of which the shell is composed, and which can conveniently be seen in a carved cameo. The outer layer, called the periostracum, is a horny brown covering of conchiolin produced in a groove between the outer and middle lobes of the mantle. It protects the shell from damage and dissolution by the acids in the sea. (If you soak a shell fragment in a weak acid solution the calcium carbonate will dissolve and only the conchiolin will be left.) Conchiolin is also the primary constituent of many opercula and a little is also present in the other shell layers.

The middle layer, known as the prismatic layer, is secreted by the outer lobe of the mantle. It consists of calcium carbonate crystals arranged horizontally, generally at right angles to the surface of the shell, so that if broken it looks dull, like broken china.

The entire surface of the mantle secretes the inner laminated layer, which is formed from overlapping plates of calcium carbonate crystals arranged vertically to parallel the outer surface of the shell. The shell's surface may be nacreous or porcelaneous; but in bivalves and gastropods is usually highly iridescent. It forms a very smooth surface that is a comfortable resting place for the sensitive and delicate mantle. If any intrusive grittiness works its way beneath the shell, such as a grain of sand or a burrowing insect, the mantle reacts by surrounding the irritant with crystals to form a pearl, which can be either nacreous or porcelaneous, like the shell. The mollusk keeps on adding to this inner layer, thickening it and making the shell heavier.

Habitat

WHEN Darwin wrote that only the fittest species survive, he meant by "fitness" the ability to produce offspring in sufficient quantities to replace the natural loss in each generation. Judged by this yardstick the mollusks are a very fit species indeed. We have already noticed that many species of mollusks appear far far back in geological time and then continue unchanged, or with very little change, right through to the present, while all sorts of inferior species have disappeared.

What has enabled the mollusks to survive and go forward to an apparently secure place in the future? One factor is their adaptability. They have successfully colonized every part of the sea, from both Poles to the Equator.

As every zone of the sea has evolved its special forms of shellfish, adapted to live in the specific conditions which it provides, it is worth looking at the different zones with some care.

Right at the top of the beach, above the tideline, where the shellfish inhabitants have to exist with only that moisture afforded by occasional spray beaten up by the wind, we find a

few specialized forms of mollusk life, such as littorinid periwinkles. From this supratidal zone the land mollusks must have at one time emerged.

The littoral zone, also known as the intertidal zone, is of course the haunt of the mollusks best known to collectors. The species in this area can rely upon an abundant supply of food and oxygen. A large number of species can develop, but they must adapt themselves to the hurly burly of the intertidal zone, which means usually growing very thick shells and selecting means of preventing themselves from being swept away from their position by the tides. Owing to the fact that they are subject to the attacks of two sets of predators, birds and animals at high tide, and fish and seals at low tide, many of them adopt special protective devices. As we have seen, an example of this is the piddocks, which excavate bunkers for themselves out of wood or stone.

Below the level of the lowest tide comes the shallow water zone which stretches to the edge of the continental shelf. Here the water is quieter and there is a good growth of seaweed, and in hot climates, coral. Many species subsist in this zone.

From the edge of the shelf to the very bottom of the sea runs the abyssal world. Only a few specialized species can inhabit this zone, and they are carnivores rather than vegetarians, as plant life dies away as the light of the sun fades. The darkness of the abyss is lit by the flashing, multi-colored lights of the cephalopods. Even a tiny species such as the ram's horn snail *(Spirula)* contributes its flashing white tail light to this carnival of light and color.

The ubiquity of the mollusk has only become a reality because mollusks are endowed with certain special qualities. One of them is the wide distribution that takes place during its larval period. As a veliger, or free-swimming sea butterfly, the young mollusk can conquer new worlds for its species, traveling freely with the ocean currents and moving with an ease and rapidity which it could never hope to emulate when encumbered by a shell. Certain

*The green turban shell (Turbo marmoratus)
and the thorny oyster, which blends unobtrusively
with its surroundings.*

larvae go through a parasitic stage and are carried about on the body of a host fish. Even mollusks that have reached the immobile or semi-mobile stage can undertake incredible journeys. Thus one mussel clung with such determination to the foot of a black duck which had stepped upon it that it not merely crushed the toe bone of the duck, but made an aerial voyage estimated at five days. Many species have become distributed in this way.

The high survival rating of the mollusk also contributes to the continuation of the species. Mollusks can go without food in a completely desiccated condition, possibly in a state of semi-animation. In one case five snails survived in the sand at the bottom of an aquarium after a period of three years and seven months during which the aquarium had been in store. No further evidence of the virtual indestructibility of the mollusk is needed than its ability to survive the experiments that have been performed upon it. These include the removal of

parts of its body, or of one of its sexes if it is a double-sexed mollusk, the amputation of part of its brain, and its bombardment with noxious substances or with electric shocks.

The most striking instance of this quality of survival, from the layman's point of view at least, is the mollusk's powers of self-regeneration. Octopuses can lose, or voluntarily relinquish, an arm, and then grow it again. Mollusks can replace their lost tentacles, regrow part of their mantle, their tails and other parts of their bodies.

Mollusks can also rebuild their shells, without, however, restoring the original color and pattern completely. Every collection should contain one of these restored shells, in which the pattern and color of the repair is at variance with the structure as a whole.

The sexual makeup of the mollusk is another help to survival. Some species alternate from one sex to the other. The edible mussel, for example, changes sex three times during its lifetime. The possibilities of fertilization are obviously increased if an isolated colony of all-male mussels can acquire females without any new members being introduced. In some species reproduction is even more fool-proof, both sexes being found in the same individual.

Reproductive ease is accompanied by an incredible fecundity. The common mussel produces millions of eggs, and there are other species that produce large numbers of progeny. It is quite possible that with the over fishing to near extinction of many of their natural predators, such as the whale and the cod, we may find ourselves faced some day with Sherlock Holmes's nightmare of the world "overrun with oysters."

The scallop (Pecten) *escapes its enemies by fast swimming, propelling itself by rapidly opening and closing its valves.*

Life Cycle

THERE is so much variation through the mollusk group that it is impossible to describe a typical mollusk way of life. Each species has evolved in an attempt to take advantage of a particular ecological niche, and the habitat, diet, locomotion and reproduction techniques of mollusks are as varied as their physiology.

All species start life as an egg, but there the differences begin. Fertilized cephalopods hatch out as miniature adults, but the other mollusks pass through two juvenile stages: the trochophore and the veliger. Sometimes these forms are free-swimming, sometimes they take place within the egg capsule. The young cowrie, for instance, turns into a minute sea butterfly which swims around by means of two large velar lobes fringed with cilia. It already has a shell—in fact two—one of which is reabsorbed into its body at the metamorphosis into adult form. The larva of the freshwater mussel has to attach itself to the skin of a fish and live parasitically before it turns into an adult.

Sometimes, as with the free-swimming larvae of the primitive gastropods, the trochophore stage lasts only for a few hours and the veliger stage can also be very brief. In more advanced mollusks this stage is longer, for the farther the veliger can travel the wider will be the distribution of the species.

The adult mollusk cannot travel so easily. It may creep along on its foot or be almost entirely stationary in a burrow or cemented to a rock. The exception is the cephalopods, which have adapted their mantles to give themselves a jet propulsion system, and can also walk along using their tentacles.

Some mollusks simply filter small food particles from the water, others draw food to themselves with their feelers. The predators will drill into living shells or, like the octopus, sit waiting to flash an arm out and claim a victim, in a bare 300th of a second. The quarry will then be crunched up by the horny beak of the octopus or squid. It rarely resists, partly because a nip from the beak injects it with paralyzing poison, partly because the tentacles themselves may give off electric shocks. The crew of the *Allecto*, a 19th-century French iron corvette that made an unsuccessful attempt to capture a giant squid, complained that they kept on getting shocks from the arms of the mollusk when they touched them.

Inner whorl section of the cephalopod Spirula peroni, *magnified ninety times. The tiny* Spirula *is a native of the deep water.*

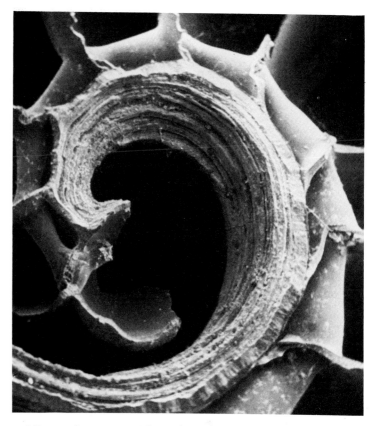

Not only can squids and octopuses change their color to match their surroundings, they also have a sac of ink which they can shoot out in a cloud, of about their own size and shape, to confuse any attacker while they lose color and jet to a safe distance. Other mollusks must depend upon their armor or their camouflage.

In most mollusks the sexes are separate, and even in hermaphroditic forms cross-fertilization is usual. In the chitons, bivalves and primitive gastropods, eggs and sperm are liberated into the water and fertilization takes place externally. They may float in the sea, or be incubated in the mantle cavity, or fixed to a rock in a mass of jelly. More advanced species are fertilized internally, sperm being passed by means of a penis in the head. In the cephalopods reproduction is more elaborate. Many species use their ability to control their color to put on mating displays, and sperm is passed along a groove in a modified tentacle into the mantle cavity of the female.

The paper nautilus, a member of the octopus family, has a particularly unusual mating. There is a striking difference between the sexes in this species: the male is little more than an inch long and has a curiously enlarged third

The octopus hunting for crabs in shallow water has made itself almost invisible by changing color to merge with the sea-bed.

arm with which it deposits its spermatophores, or packets of sperm. It places the arm, known as the *hectocotylus,* in the mantle of the much larger female and then swims away – leaving the hectocotylus behind! The eggs are laid by the female into a finely fashioned and fragile shell of great beauty which is much sought after by collectors. It is not a shell in the normal sense, for it is not secreted by a mantle but by glands on the edge of the webs bordering the first pair of arms. It may serve as a protection, for the animal could crawl into it (though its fragility makes this use doubtful), and it may act as a float, but its main purpose is that of an egg case: it is in this "shell" that the eggs are incubated.

Right *The common octopus* (Octopus vulgaris), *awaiting its prey.*

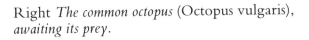

The crew of the French corvette, Allecto, at grips with a gigantic squid.

In other octopuses the eggs are usually attached to the roof of a cave, where, after the hatching, the female watches over her brood to guard them from predators, which include other octopuses. Even free-swimming species like the octopus may lay as many as 50,000 eggs. Immobile species produce many more: the edible mussel *(Mytilus edulis)* may spawn as many as 12 million eggs from a single mating.

The common octopus has a reputation for attacking swimmers, though such occurrences are in fact uncommon. It is easy to see why the creature is feared; the suckers give it such a firm grip that they are sometimes torn away when their prey attempts to escape.

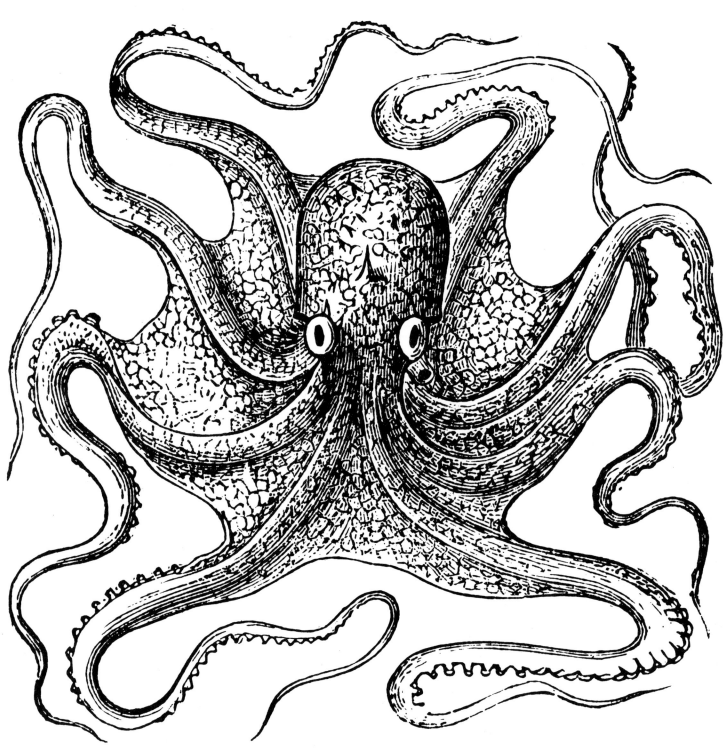

The paper nautilus (Argo argonautica), *a member of the octopus family. The main use of the "shell" shown here is as an egg case.*

Strange Shells

SHELL collectors who like unusual shells need go no farther than the nearest American beach. There they will find a wide variety of very strange shellfish. Take the moon snails for example. These are some of the best-known of all shells to beach-goers because of the collar-shaped cases of eggs that they lay on the sand. Seen crawling along a sandy flat, the moon snail looks more like a bulldozer than a shellfish, as it has a long *propodium* pushed out in front of it. Two tentacles wave above the large gray foot of the shell as it digs its way through the sand, looking for clams and smaller shellfish. Once found, small shellfish are efficiently drilled into by the moon snail. An acid secreted from a small gland near the tip of the proboscis softens the shell ready for the snail to get to work with its radula, which bores into the shell and then, like a flexible vacuum cleaner nozzle, sucks out the prey's vital juices.

Even more unusual in appearance are the conches, or *Strombidae*. Although some of them

have the toughest shells in existence (you could jump on them without doing them any harm), the queen conch, paradoxically, yields one of the most fragile jewels in existence – the cameo. The delicate cameos carved from this shell are so soft that the designs carved on them will wear away when merely rubbed by a soft fabric.

An extraordinary feature of the conches is their brightly colored eyes which project on stalks. The eyes vary from species to species: each one has its own characteristic colors arranged in concentric circles.

The abalone *(Haliotis),* another shell found in American waters, has the unique feature of a series of holes formed along the outer edge of its shell. Through these holes it extrudes deoxygenated water and thrusts long feelers. As the shell grows, it seals one row of holes and forms a new set near to the new front edge. How the abalone prevents predators from taking advantage of these breaches in its armor is one of nature's mysteries.

An oyster that lives in trees sounds like a fantasy from a medieval traveler's tale. How-

ever, trees *are* the habitat of the flat tree oyster *(Isognomon alatus),* which lives on the lower branches of mangroves in Florida. Like many other types of shells, the flat tree oyster has acclimatized itself to living with just a little moisture, mostly that provided by spray or exceptionally high water, such as flood tides. It is much safer out of the water because it is well removed from all marine predators.

A wide variety of unusual shells is also to be found on the British seashore, including a particularly good selection of home-building shells, surely some of the most eccentric of all varieties.

The rough-shelled gaping file *(Lima hians)* builds itself a nest in water from twelve to forty fathoms deep. It is constructed under large stones and consists of fragments of old shell, pieces of stone, bits of nullipore, and shreds of

wood, all lashed together with pieces of the byssus with which the file shell anchors itself to the foundation of its home. The adult file shell lives by itself in a nest of this sort, the younger ones often sharing a nest in a group. The gaping file even has the help of tenant creatures, usually a tiny porcelain crab and a marine worm which live in symbiosis with it and keep the nest clean. File shells are usually rather dull in appearance, but the live mollusk has a mass of long colorful tentacles which extend all around the edges of the shell when it is swimming.

Another interesting British homebuilder is the wood-boring piddock. Also found in Continental waters, it nearly brought about the obliteration of large areas of the reclaimed Netherlands by drilling into the wooden piles supporting the dykes that kept the sea from flooding Holland. Only just in time to save

Left *The cone shells (Toxoglossa) are the most poisonous of all marine creatures. Their sting causes death by paralysis of the nervous system.*

Right *The dye murex (Murex brandaris) was once the source of the richest and most expensive purple dye.*

Below *The top shell, a beautiful example of iridescence.*

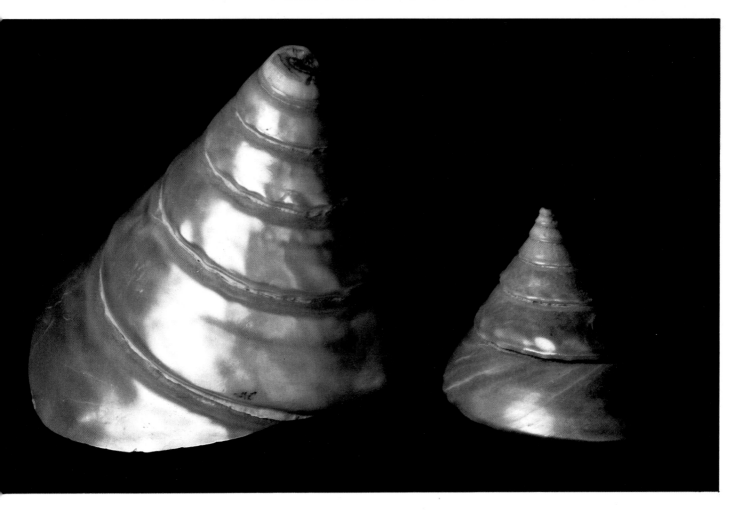

the dams from bursting, the Dutch discovered that if they soaked wooden timbers in a strong solution of iron oxide the piddocks would be discouraged from boring into them.

Equally destructive is the ship worm or *Teredo navalis,* a deep-boring mollusk, which despite its name is not a worm. It bores its way deeply into any wood exposed under water, and the whole history of shipbuilding is one of unavailing struggles against the Teredo. In the time of the Emperor Claudius, who made Britain a province of the Roman Empire, the Romans sheathed the imperial galleys in thin lead sheeting which they painted over with tar mixed with hair, which was then sandwiched by another layer of lead on top. Shipbuilders of the 18th century felt that they had at last won a victory over the ship worm by covering the hulls with copper plates.

Another interesting home-building shell is the flask shell, which sets up a home shaped like a bottle, with a crooked neck. The flask-like structure is cemented all over with little stones, old shells, shell fragments and sand.

Poisonous shells always exert a fascination over people's minds. Few people are deterred from eating edible mussels by the fact that they can, on occasion, secrete a deadly poison. Schenck, the great toxicologist, has pointed out that mussel poison is a twin of that other marine poison, the venom of the globe fish.

Judging by the effects of these poisons, they are very similar to that employed by the most toxic of all shells, the *Toxoglossa* group. Shells such as the *Turridae, Terebridae,* and *Conidae* all possess a poison gland, attached to a poison sac, and located next to the stomach inside the dorsal wall of the body cavity. They administer their poison by means of a bite from a radular tooth, shaped like a harpoon, enclosed in a proboscis, rather like a hypodermic needle.

The Toxoglossa use this poison to paralyze and kill other invertebrates on which they feed. The symptoms of the poison in humans are swelling, a burning pain, and a creeping numbness, followed in severe cases by paralysis, dumbness and partial blindness.

Above *The ship-worm—in fact not a worm but a mollusk—was a continual threat to wooden ships.*

Right *A font in the church of St. Sulpice, Paris, made from a giant clam.*

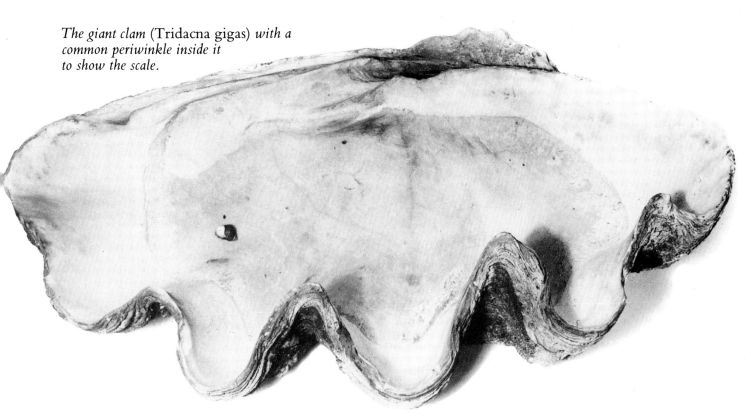

The giant clam (Tridacna gigas) *with a common periwinkle inside it to show the scale.*

Giants and Pygmies

STRICTLY speaking the giant of all mollusks is the giant squid, which has a rudimentary shell concealed in its rubbery body. However, it is very unlikely that anyone would want to collect a giant squid; what is much more likely is that, if they were to meet, the squid would collect *him*. The Goliath of the mollusks is generally taken to be the giant clam *(Tridacna gigas)* which can easily reach a weight of 150 pounds. The biggest recorded specimen weighed 507 pounds. Its two valves fit into one another, in a sinuous, serpentine saw-tooth design, like the jaws of the giant mantraps used by Victorian squires to catch poachers. A mantrap is exactly what the giant clam can be if reputations are anything to go on. Many tales are told in the South Pacific about unwary fishermen who set foot on these monsters, only to have them snap their valves shut on the fishermen's ankles. A mollusk that measures 4 feet 6 inches long would have no mechanical difficulties in holding down a man for as long as it liked. The only question is, why should the algae-eating giant clam want to trap humans? It certainly makes a brilliant enough display with its mantle to attract anything unwary to come near it.

Seen through the water the mantle, as glimpsed between its gaping valves, is a beautiful kaleidoscope. The colors vary, sometimes green, blue, and red, sometimes olive green or brown with vivid emerald green "eyes." Unlike most other mollusks the giant clam sits with its valves gaping. Giant clams, except when buried under boulders, lie on the hinge side so as to be able to open and close their valves. Young tridacnas are anchored to their position by means of a byssus; the older ones maintain it simply by means of their enormous weight.

Partly because of its size, partly because of the fine material which can be obtained from the valves, South Sea islanders prized the giant clam as a cistern to collect water from Pandanus trees during rain. They also used it

Below *This group of tiny shells from all over the world provides an interesting contrast with the giants, such as the clam shell on page 39.*

Bottom *The living giant clam, whose colorful mantle attracts its prey.*

Shells of the fossil gastropod Turritella sulcifera *in sandstone from England's Bracklesham Beds, of Eocene times.*

as a bucket and carved it to make the war standards for their canoes and the beautiful ornaments called "*kap kaps.*" Today's visitors to the haunts of the *Tridacna tridacna*, such as the Great Barrier Reef, hope they may find some of the famous Tridacna pearls.

When it comes to the other end of the scale, the pygmy shells, there is almost too wide a choice. Most of the known species of shells are less than half an inch in length and some are microscopic. The type of ultra-small shell that will perhaps occur to most people, the *Foraminifera*, is not a molluskan one. *Foraminifera* (the word means "hole-bearing") are a form of marine invertebrates, which have contributed to build up the chalk cliffs of England, and which still make up the sand on some well-known beaches.

Though to the specialist collector who owns a microscope ultra-miniature shells are a delightful subject, the smallest shell that the average collector is likely to become interested in is one about a quarter of an inch to half an inch in size. Nature has been very obliging in providing an enormous quantity of shells of just that size. Something like 90,000 shells of the 100,000 species known are

half an inch or less. There are many delightful small shells, such as the sea snail (*Neritina communis*) from the Philippines, which is brilliantly striped in yellow, red, and black. *Columbella fulgurans,* also from the Philippines, is a little like one of the poisonous yet lovely cone shells without the venom. *Bankivia fasciata* from Australia is a lovely little spire, while *Cantharidus irisodontes*, also from Australia, is a delightful irregularly coiled shell.

A typical small mollusk is the British spotted cowrie (*Trivia monacha*). It is found between tide marks under rocks and ledges, among the tiny organisms, such as compound ascidians, on which it feeds. It breeds in the late spring and summer, laying its eggs in vase-shaped capsules that are the remains of the minute sea squirts which it has already eaten. Each capsule, about a quarter of an inch in height, contains several hundred bright orange eggs.

Because cowries feed on animals fixed more or less on one spot, they are slower-moving than many of the other carnivores, traveling no more than 6 inches in a minute. But in the mantle cavity they have a well-developed sense organ, called the osphradium, which is thought to be sensitive to traces of material

A group of small shells: spindle shell (left), Turritella (top and right), *and bubble shells* (middle).

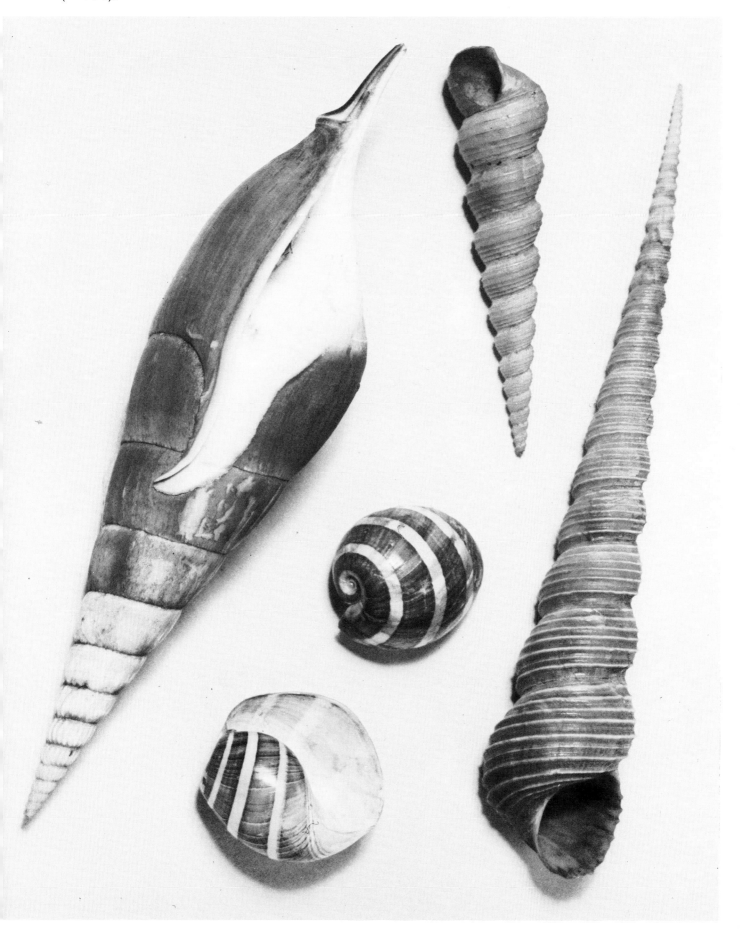

Two fossil ammonites: Parkinsonia Dorsetensis
(right), *and* (left) Asteroceras obtusum,
cut in half to show the chambers.

dissolved in the water, and helps cowries to locate their prey.

Unlike most other mollusk shells, the cowrie does not have a periostracum layer over the outside, presumably because in life the shell is almost always covered by the mantle. This means that the shell has a high polish.

Although they are so small, microscopic shells are studied even more closely than their full-scale relatives. This is because certain types of very small fossil shells are associated with oil deposits. All oil companies employ a paleontologist whose task it is to scrutinize under a microscope the samples of rock brought up from a bore hole to see if they contain those shells.

Living shells are just as good indicators of particular localities as their fossil relatives. A famous Prussian detective once solved a case involving a stolen shipment of wine by discovering minute shells, which could only have come from a certain beach, along with a re-packed bottle of the stolen wine.

How Shells Developed

THE mollusks are one of the animal kingdom's oldest families. The earliest mollusk, as reconstructed by paleontologists, was a limpet-like gastropod, with a big foot, radula and most of the usual organs. In fact it bears a close resemblance to that "living fossil," *Neopilina galatheae* (see page 11).

The first gastropods appear in Cambrian times, more than 600 million years ago, and almost as far back as one can go in geological time. Since the Cambrian, more than 15,000 fossil gastropods have been discovered, and there are probably many more waiting to be found.

The non-molluskan brachiopods, or lamp shells, also made an early start in life at about the same time. There are no fewer than 30,000 fossil species of brachiopods, beginning in the Cambrian and going on to present-day times. By contrast with fossil species, existing species have shrunk to a mere 200.

A slab of limestone crowded with fossil ammonites from the Lower Jurassic strata.

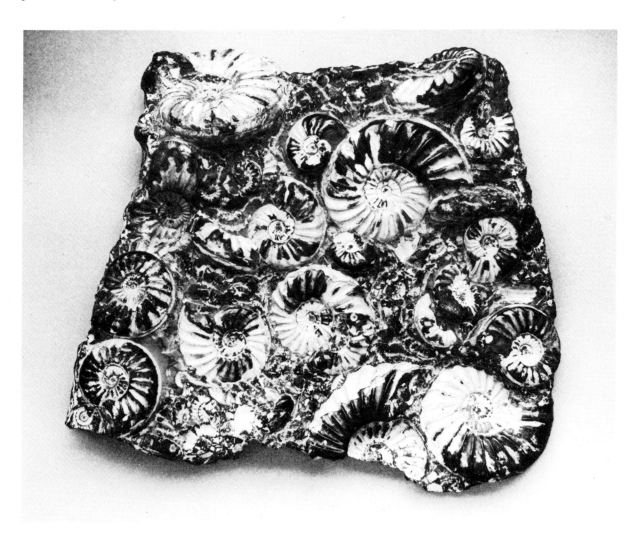

Cephalopods also have such a long history that existing species are often referred to as "living fossils." The nautiloids, still represented by species whose shells are cherished collectors' pieces, begin in mid-Cambrian times, about 550 million years ago. On the way to the present time they throw out two interesting cadet families, the ammonites and the belemnites. It is from the latter family that the octopuses and squids of today descend.

The Ordovician period was probably the time when mollusks had the most important place in creation. It lasted from 500 million to 425 million years ago and has been named "The Age of Shellfish." Enormous squids, such as *Endoceras*, dominated the Ordovician seabeds and preyed on the echinoids, asteroids and crinoids. Slow-moving ammonites left a wiggly trail behind them in the mud, in contrast to other cephalopods, such as *Orthonybyoceras* which left a straight one.

Fast streamlined belemnites, such as *Sactoceras*, shaped like armor-piercing bullets, hurtled by, arms waving, in immense swarms. Gastropods such as the snail *Machurites* crawled along the bottom, next to *Cyclonema*, which looked like a modern whelk. At this time the bivalves were represented by species such as *Rafinesquina*, much less spectacular than the cephalopods.

This was the last age in which shellfish were the dominant species. By the Silurian period other forms, such as trilobites, had taken over. New species of shellfish continued to emerge, among them further variations of the ammonites, which continued to diversify during the Carboniferous period, growing in some instances to the size of a cartwheel.

The length of geological time reminds us of the incredible survival power of the mollusks. Many modern species have survived unchanged from an era so remote as to be almost meaningless in human time conceptions. As we have seen, the *Neopilina*, believed to have become a fossil 600 million years ago, has now been found alive. There may be other ancient species still to be discovered.

The seas of Cretaceous times, an era which began 135 million years ago, and which lasted for 72 million years, were exceptionally rich in shellfish. They included oysters and scallops very like our own varieties, belemnites like *Baculites,* the *Helioceras,* an ammonite with a shell like a corkscrew staircase, and *Placenticeras,* a nautiloid like the present-day nautili. There were hosts of other shellfish, such as gastropods like *Turritella,* and all these creatures after their death left their shells to join the shells of *Foraminifera,* spicules from sponges and chitons, and carapaces of other sea creatures to make the minute grains of calcium carbonate of which chalk is composed.

Although the Cretaceous seas were fairly shallow, a few hundred feet deep, about the same as the North Sea today, over millions of years the deposits of chalk built up to thicknesses greater than the depth of the seas which originally laid them down.

Shelly limestone is another gift from the fossil past of mollusks. Cerithium limestone is a stone composed of the innumerable shells of a fossil gastropod which persisted from Jurassic to recent times. It had a tall, spiraling shell ornamented by whorls, which reached a maximum height of about five inches. Often all that remains of the gastropods is the cast of their shell, which leaves a mark as though an auger had been bored into the stone. Too porous to be used for exterior work, this species of limestone is nevertheless prized for its ornamental qualities.

Unusual Uses for Shells

MOST of us have worn buttons made of mother-of-pearl, but this is only one instance of the part played by shells in the history of man's apparel. Some American Indian tribes, for example, used shells to protect their genitals when forcing a way through the dense undergrowth of forests, all other parts of their body being left naked. A similar shell covering is also used by natives of the South Pacific. Although a normal part of masculine dress, it is ornamented with the fine workmanship which characterizes shell art in that part of the world.

From the pierced and polished shells that New Stone Age man strung into necklaces 35,000 years ago to the present day, shells have been used for personal ornament. In early times most of this "jewelry" was made from the shells of edible mollusks, but often rare shells are found far inland, which shows the importance that their owners placed upon them. Headdresses, bangles, belts and even skirts have been made from shells. Sometimes a particular kind of shell, such as the golden cowrie in the Central Pacific, was considered suitable only for persons of high rank.

Large shells have been used as containers for all kinds of things. The "false trumpet" *(Syrinx aruana)* was used to carry water by the

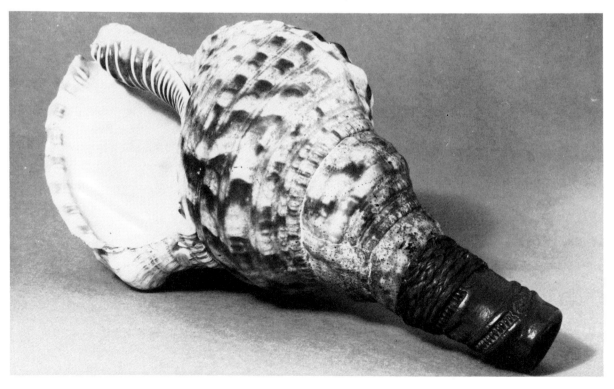

A triton shell mounted as a Buddhist temple trumpet.

Aborigines of northwestern Australia and the natives of New Guinea. A hole made in the first whorl of this largest of the gastropod shells gave a thumb hold which made it comfortable to carry, and a full-grown specimen could hold a three-quarter gallon of water. The baler shells *(Melo)* as one might guess from their name, were used for bailing out small boats. On a smaller scale the mussel known as *Unio pictorum* was used until the beginning of our own century as a container for holding artists' colors. Although the gold and silver used by calligraphers for illuminating is no longer sold in this kind of mussel shell, it is still called "shell gold." Other special kinds of shells, such as the nautilus, have always been used as cups. The goblets of the Norse kings were made from the *Turbo olearius.*

Mankind long ago discovered that the shell is the only self-playing musical instrument. If you hold a large univalve, such as a dog whelk, to your ear, you will hear the legendary "Song of the Sea." This is an echoing murmur, caused by the reflection of the noises of the human body, magnified and reduplicated, from the hollow of the shell.

Once the discovery had been made that shells are naturally sonorous, men soon capitalized on this property by using them as trumpets. If a hole is cut in some large gastropod shells, sometimes near the apex, sometimes

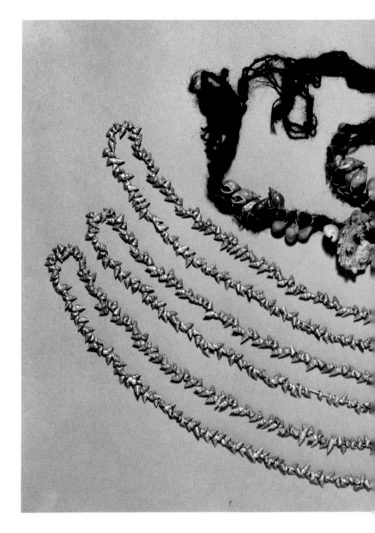

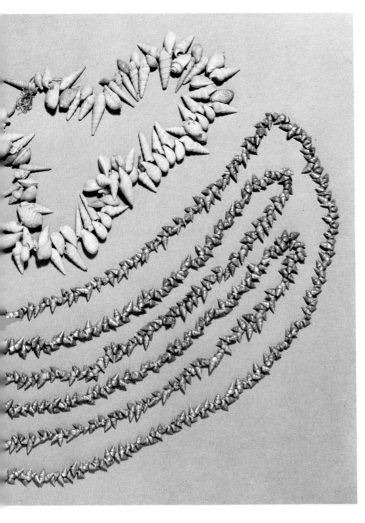

on the body whorl, they can be blown to produce a deep booming note that can be heard over long distances. The most famous of all these trumpet shells is the sacred chank, also known as the conch (in fact it is not related to the queen conch).

Conches were fished, at great risk, by stone divers in the torrid waters of the Coromandel coast. The best specimens were kept for the service of the temple, where they sounded the hours of the services. They were also used for pouring libations. A *dextral* or right-hand-coiling conch was considered to be so sacred that it was worshiped as a manifestation of the Deity. Conch shell trumpets were blown by Hindu warriors in the Indian epics. Each hero had his own trumpet and each trumpet had its name, among them Panchajanya, the trumpet of the god Krishna. Vishnu, the preserver, is also generally depicted holding a chank in one of his four arms. Victory was awarded to whoever sounded this trumpet, and the association of the chank with these gods explains the veneration with which it is regarded.

Right down to the present day the melancholy note of the conch trumpet echoes from mountaintop temples in Nepal, or breaks the silence of the night as a Buddhist hermit signals his unsleeping devotion. Shinto priests in Japan also blow conches to tell the charitably inclined that they are coming.

Above *Shell necklaces from Tasmania.*

Left *A sacred chank-shell trumpet from Tibet, mounted in gold, set with turquoise and coral.*

Right *Shell-work ornaments were popular in the 18th and 19th centuries. An elaborate grotto such as this must have taken years to complete.*

A pearl-shell belt and pubic cover from Tasmania.

The resonance of shell was also put to good use in the ancient Near East. Castanets or clappers were fashioned from Tridacna shells in Nimrud in Assyrian times, while in ancient Sumer the mosaic artists made use of the sonorousness of shell by ornamenting the sound boxes of lyres with shell and lapis lazali mosaics.

It was a short step for artists and craftsmen to discover that shells were not merely a source of ready-made units which could be adapted to all sorts of purposes, they were also a quarry for ideas.

Their hard, white, impervious, glassy nature inevitably made men want to imitate the substance of shells in some artificial compound. This is just what happened when porcelain was discovered in China. Our word "porcelain," by the way, comes from the Italian word for a particular kind of shell called a "little pig."

The resonance of shells is echoed in the shape of the Greek theater, which is marvelously designed acoustically, and which is shaped rather like a shallow pecten shell, with the stage just where the valve of the shell is. The most amazing sonic device ever to have been based upon the structure of a shell must have been an enormous sound conductor designed by the Jesuit inventor, Athanasius Kircher, in the 17th century. It was built upon the model of the Triton shell. The mouth of the "shell," which took up a vast amount of space, opened on to the courtyard of a palace. Its tip ended in the private chamber of the owner of the palace. There he could sit and listen to the sounds of people talking in the open air, magnified a hundred times.

Long before the French naturalist Lamarck told architects that they would find many lessons in shells, particularly as regards the treatment of surfaces, designers had been aware of their possibilities. Eighteenth-century architects had placed scallop-shaped sound reflectors over the top of pulpits in churches, so that the preachers' words could be carried more effectively to the congregation sitting at the back of the church. Architects of the same period had developed the beautiful shell-shaped porches to town houses. The shell has been a very widely used motif in architecture as far back as Coptic Egypt, while, still in Egypt, the revolving spiral of turreted shells may have suggested the most famous of Arab minarets, that of Ibn Tulun in Cairo.

Shells in Art

"SHELL art" immediately suggests the arrangement of shells in attractive patterns, and especially the beautiful shell flowers which were made in the Rococo period. But shell and shells have been used in many more ways than this, providing the raw material and the inspiration for some of the world's finest craftsmanship.

As far back as Neolithic times, the inhabitants of Palestine were using the tusk shell to make strings of beads, as early people used beads all over the world. In Jericho, one of the world's most ancient cities, they modeled plaster heads over the skulls of their honored ancestors and chose cowries with staringly contrasted spots, like the pupils of eyes, to insert into their empty sockets.

Seven thousand years before Christ the craftsmen of Palestine had begun to carve pearl shell. Today some of the finest pearl-shell carvings made still come from the Holy Land, where in Bethlehem craftsmen continue a tradition which they claim was taught to their ancestors by the Crusaders but which clearly has much more ancient roots. Rosaries, crucifixes, medals and other beautiful pearl-shell carvings are made, and many of them are sold outside the Church of the Holy Sepulcher in Jerusalem and in Bethlehem. Like those the Crusaders took home with them, these carvings were for centuries laid upon the altar and blessed, to become treasured relics in some far distant land. As late as 1911 they were still regarded by Russian pilgrims as safeguards against every evil.

In the third millennium BC shell decoration flowered at Ur of the Chaldees. The elaborate shell and gem mosaics on statues, gaming boards, the sounding boxes of lyres, and the pillars and walls of temples and palaces are among the most impressive works of this ancient civilization.

Four thousand years later and on the other side of the world, the Mixtec and Aztec civilizations that flourished in North America between the early Middle Ages of Europe and the Renaissance also produced wonderful shell mosaics. The Spanish conquistadors who overthrew the ancient Mexican empire stood amazed at the virtuosity of the Aztec shell carvers, who covered temples, idols, masks, helmets, jewelry and many other articles with a mosaic composed of pecten shells, clam shells, mother-of-pearl, turquoise, jet, and glittering precious stones. All the largest works in shell have unfortunately disappeared, such as the rooms of the Temple at Tula, which were covered with shells fitted together with silver, but a few small mosaics have miraculously survived. They were taken back to Europe and preserved in a museum in Florence until the curator threw them out in 1819. Most of these Aztec mosaics were then bought by British collectors.

Gaming board inlaid in shell from Ur of Chaldees.

51

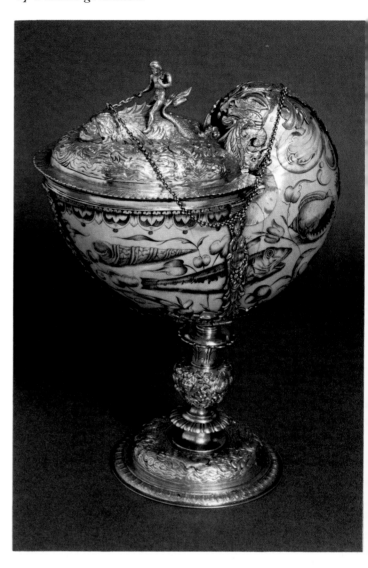

The Frewin Cup, made in the 18th century from a nautilus shell, richly engraved, and set in gold by a master goldsmith.

About a century after the last Aztec shell mosaics were made, a new kind of shell carving was developed in China. The Chinese craftsmen made goblets out of entire nautilus shells which they carved all over in low relief and then carefully engraved. Some of the periostracum of the shell was left uncarved, producing a cameo-like effect. These beautiful cups were imported to Europe and set in gold by Renaissance goldsmiths. They introduced the idea of nautilus carving to western craftsmen. During the 17th and 18th centuries many goblets were made, sometimes for use, more usually for display.

Many of them originated in Holland, where there were very keen shell collectors who would pay almost as much for a paper nautilus or a "Little Skipper" as they would for a rare tulip. The Belkein family, who had originated as carvers of mother-of-pearl plaques to set in gun mountings, kept the connoisseurs of The Hague and Amsterdam supplied with the greatest masterpieces in shell carvings ever produced. The Belkeins and their imitators carved mother-of-pearl plaques for snuff or tobacco boxes or framed pictures, and engraved them in thin line engraving, which was then darkened by pigment made from coal dust and oil. They sculpted whole nautilus shells into daring creations in which the periostracum was left on the surface in a series of knot-work designs, like contemporary embroidery. The knurl of the nautilus shell was carved into a miniature sculpture, such as a mouse or a face, and the rounded chambers into opened-out designs. Another very popular decoration was to carve a knight's helmet with closed visor just above the edge of the lip of the shell. Beautiful engravings adorn the sides of the Belkein nautili.

The success of the Belkeins encouraged carvers of other nations to decorate nautilus shells. For the Great Exhibition of 1851 in London an industrious working man named John Wood exhibited a nautilus shell at the Crystal Palace. It was, said one newspaper, "dedicated to the memory of Nelson. Upon the front is represented a globe, with Britannia seated upon the Lion, and possessed of the usual emblems of sovereignty . . . Upon one side of the shell is a representation of Peace, seated on the prow of the vessel, pointing to the victories achieved by the hero, and upon the other is represented George and the Dragon." All this, and much more, Wood carved with an ordinary penknife.

Pearl-shell carving continued to flourish

A nautilus shell engraved by Jan Belkein in the 17th century. The Belkein family of Holland originated this art form, and their success encouraged other artists to carve shells.

A superb example of the elaborate shell
arrangements popular in the Victorian age.

during the 17th century, when Jan and Jerémie Belkein, Jean Gaulette, J. Hercules, and Dirk Van Ryswyck all produced lovely nacre carvings.

Lavish artistry in mother-of-pearl was also applied to the gun stocks for expensive sporting rifles made in Germany and Bohemia during this period. It consisted chiefly of nacre plaques that were sunk into the ebony, walnut, snakewood, or palisander wooden stocks. The same craftsmen who decorated guns also produced pearl inlaid furniture.

By the 18th century pearl-shell carving was a declining art, the last pearl-shell carver worth mentioning being Jan Bernard Barckhuyzen. In the Far East, however, the Chinese evolved "scratch-carved" mother-of-pearl card markers. These were made purely for the European market, as the Chinese did not play whist or "Pope Joan," games for which the markers were used. They were made up in sets of a gross. Many of them were fish-shaped, hence their name of "fish." These markers were very lightly and delicately engraved with microscopic scenes of Chinese life. They are some of the most exquisite works of art ever produced in any material. There are still many of them to be bought, though the price is rising.

Mother-of-pearl also served as one of the principal materials for inlay in lacquer in Japan and China, and also in Birmingham, England, where it was cut and shaped to inlay in the papier mâché objects produced in such large quantities in Victorian England (see illustration on page 61).

Shells as Currency

THE expression "shell out!" is one that must have been understood by peoples of all countries at all times throughout history. It is really only in our own day, since money cowries used as counters in school to teach children to do their sums have been replaced with plastic beads, that shells have lost their association with money.

Shells were probably first used as counters as soon as man learned to think of figures higher than ten, but the first recorded time that they were officially used as currency was under the Shang Dynasty (1765–1122 BC), in ancient China. The shells used were cowries from the far-off Chinese coast, and they were rare and expensive objects. They were pierced and strung on cords, so that when the Chinese adopted coins it seemed natural that they too should have a hole pierced in the middle and be carried on strings. This usage survived until comparatively recently.

Long before the cowrie shell, or *Cypraea moneta,* stopped being a coinage in China it had been adopted as a currency by many other primitive societies. In Africa cowries remained acceptable for payments down to modern times, many Africans preferring to accept them rather than cash. After all, they were impossible to counterfeit, as well as being portable and decorative. Many Africans carried their worldly goods about with them as bracelets and anklets.

In other parts of the world other shells have been used for money. Until a century ago the Nagas of Assam used the chank as currency, and tusk-shell money was used by Indians of

be carved from a quahog than purple ones, the purple were scarcer—hence their higher value. In 1640 the infant colony of Massachusetts laid down the rate of exchange. "White to pass at four, and blue at two a penny." Wampum was arranged in long strings of a fathom or six feet in length. Its value depended solely on the labor lavished upon making it. Anyone could find quahog shells, break them into pieces small enough to grind, bore the pieces with a drill, string them on the sinews of a deer, and grind the pieces by hand into tubular beads between two rubbing stones. Of course this was a lot of hard work, so hard that genuine wampum made in colonial days has begun to rise in price as no more of it is being made.

The Indians were very glad to acquire from the Pilgrim Fathers some European tools which made wampum making an easier task. Many of the colonists paid for their land with payments which included tools of this sort. The settlement of East Hampton was bought in 1648 for a hundred "mucksucks," as the Indians called awl blades, for boring wampum. No doubt they were a great improvement on the flint drills the Indians had used previously.

The Pilgrims were not slow to realize the value of wampum, but it took them a long time to puzzle out a quick and effective way of making perfect beads. The Indian set little value on his time. He did not care how long he spent grinding shell, but the colonists had more commercial attitudes to time and effort. Eventually the Dutch introduced a method of wampum making that was almost certainly copied from the methods used by the women coral bead makers of Torre del Greco at Naples. Wampum continued to be made by hand, mostly by women, till as late as 1844. In Bergen, New Jersey, many industrious girls supported their families by making the shell coins for traders who wanted to take an acceptable currency with them to the American Far West. Then suddenly someone hit on the method of mass-producing ceramic wampum, and the old hand-made beads disappeared.

Wampum was used as jewelry and to decorate clothing, such as an embroidered deerskin given by Powhatan, the father of Pocahontas, to an English friend. It was also used to convey messages and record treaties. Belts of purple, white, and black wampum were woven on sinew threads, and taken on embassies by Indian diplomats. The patterns on the belts were symbolic. Thus the Five Nations of the Iroquois would be represented

the American west coast from Alaska down to California. The abalone was used by other American Indians, but in this case the shell was not used in its original state but cut and worked.

The shell currency of North America's eastern seaboard was even more elaborate. Known as wampum, it was a very sophisticated currency indeed. It did not consist of natural shells; every single piece had to be carefully carved out by the wampum maker. The word "wampum" means "a string of white beads," and this is exactly what it was, long tabular white beads—or purple beads, which were much more valuable. The beads were made from the shell of the quahog, or *Venus mercenaria*. This clam is heart-shaped and about three inches across. The inside of the shell is white, the border purple, like the toga of a Roman senator. As more white beads could

Below *A selection of cowries. The reason for their bright colors remains a mystery: they are never seen during life.*

Right *A beautiful example of mother-of-pearl inlay on a Japanese box.*

by five diamonds, symbolizing their council fires. Sometimes these belts were very long. Pontiac, the Indian chief who planned to exterminate the whites in America, had a belt six feet four inches in length on which the names of the forty-seven tribes who had allied themselves with him were recorded.

Such belts served as a memorandum to the ambassadors about what they were to say in their harangue to *Corlaer* (the Indian name for the Governor of New York) or whomever was the opposite party in the negotiation. At suitable pauses during the oration, the speaker would hand over another belt of wampum. These belts were so valuable that they were not retained; they were handed back to the donors and then stored in the tribal archives as a record of what had been agreed.

Right *Belts of wampum, made from the quahog, and used as money by the North American Indians.*

56

Shell Gems

Above *Money cowries* (Cypraea moneta) *strung on coconut fiber for trading purposes.*

THE pearl is the supreme gem of the sea, and it is the only one of the many mollusk wonders that man has really made his own by learning to control the creation of artificially stimulated or "cultured" pearls. The great botanist Linnaeus, to whom we owe the system of plant and animal classification, and who did considerable work on mollusks, was awarded a patent of nobility by the king of Sweden, but not because of his scientific achievements. He was given the honor because he had shown the Crown how to create cultured pearls by boring the shell of an oyster with a silver wire. The Scandinavian fjords, with their isolated pools or "polls" at the head, communicating with the sea only at high tide, make ideal breeding places for the oyster. However, the experiment suggested by Linnaeus came to nothing.

The discovery that pearl production could be stimulated was made in China in the 13th

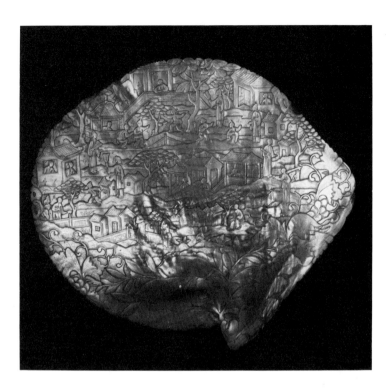
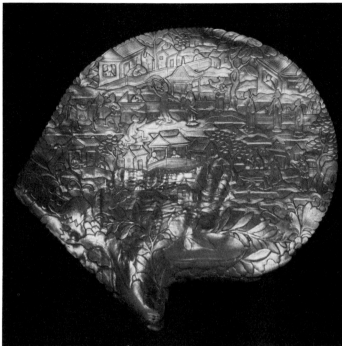

century. Chinese cultured pearls were usually attached to the nacreous inner lining of the shell and consequently needed the addition of a half sphere of mother-of-pearl to form the joined rounded pearl known as a doublet.

The Chinese inserted tiny figurines within the shell of the fresh-water mussel, returning the mussel to its bed for about three years for the figurine to become encased in pearl.

The production of well-shaped cultured pearls was developed in Japan where Kokichi Mikimoto set up the first pearl farm in the Bay of Ago in 1890. His research showed that a very small mother-of-pearl bead was the most successful irritant to stimulate pearl production. The first cultured pearls that could pass for the genuine thing were produced in this way in 1894, but they did not appear on the market until 1921. To prevent rejection by the mollusk, the bead is wrapped in a piece of tissue cut from the mantle of the oyster in which it is then placed. Japan now has more than 300 sea farms producing cultured pearls.

A faultless pearl is one of the oldest symbols of perfection, and has been valued since ancient times. In classical Rome only citizens of high rank were allowed to wear pearls, and Pliny refers to them as "the richest merchandise of all, and the most sovereign commodity in the whole world." A special corporation existed to control the trade whose members were known as *margaritarii*.

It is ironic to reflect that this coveted gem, so sought after by men, for which so much

blood has been spilled, starts life as nothing but a nuisance to its mollusk creator. All shells are capable of producing pearls, but only those with iridescent linings such as the common oyster *(Ostrea edulis)* the horse mussel *(Modiola vulgaris)* and the edible mussel *(Mytilus edulis)* produce the nacreous variety of pearls which is so desirable. In fact the common oyster rarely produces lustrous pearls and they are usually black or purple in color. The finest pearls come from genus *Meleagrina* (or *Pinctada*, formerly known as *Margaritifera*), the best among them being those produced by the Mohar found in the Persian Gulf. The best-known pearl oyster occurs only in tropical waters, but you do not have to go to the Middle East or the South Pacific to find beautiful pearls. Oysters in the Gulf of California, the Gulf of Mexico and in the waters of Mexico's west coast produce high-quality pearls including some dark pearls with a metallic sheen. Freshwater mussels, especially *Unio margaritifera*, which live in the rivers and streams of the northern temperate countries, can produce fine pearls. In the United States excellent pearls have come from the Mississippi River and its tributaries, and the most famous American pearl, weighing $23\frac{1}{4}$ carats, came from a stream near Paterson, New Jersey, in 1857. It was bought by Tiffany, the jeweler, and was eventually sold to the Empress Eugenie of France.

Britain has produced some fine pearls too. The rivers of Scotland yield a beautiful crop

A cameo carved on a helmet shell.

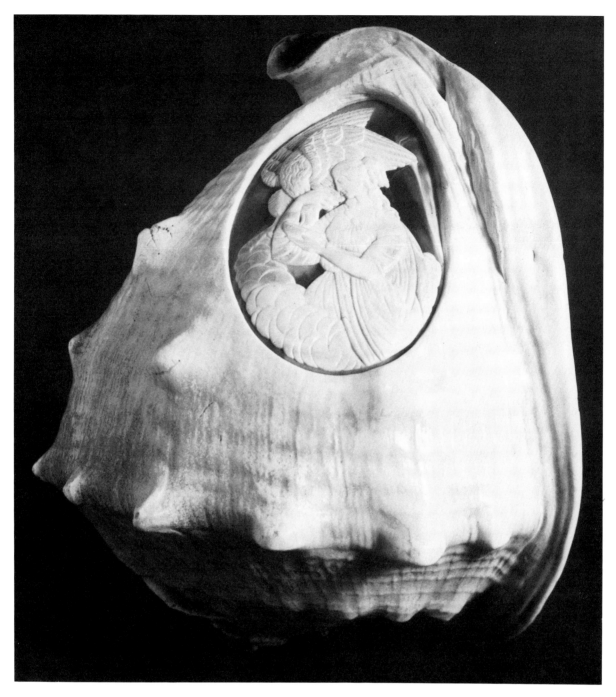

of pastel colored pearls every year, and those of Cumberland and Wales would provide the rich harvest that they did of old if only pollution could be stopped and the mussel re-established in their waters.

The mantle of the shell has the power of repairing any damage done to the interior of the shell, damage such as the attack of a minute boring insect, or even the infiltration of a grain of sand, which causes torment to the sensitive flesh of the animal. To deal with this intrusion, shellfish cover over the intruder with layers of nacreous material deposited by the mantle. Once covered over, the mantle continues,

adding more material, so that year by year the pearl gets bigger and bigger.

The sphere thus formed inside the shellfish takes on the iridescent splendor of the nacreous shell of the mollusk. There is no difference between mother-of-pearl and pearls, except that mother-of-pearl is plentiful and pearls are few and rare. As the English navigator, shell collector, and buccaneer, William Dampier, pointed out in the 17th century, mother-of-pearl is just as brilliant as any pearl. So much is a pearl part of its mother-of-pearl background that the mother-of-pearl often engulfs it and covers it over completely. This may

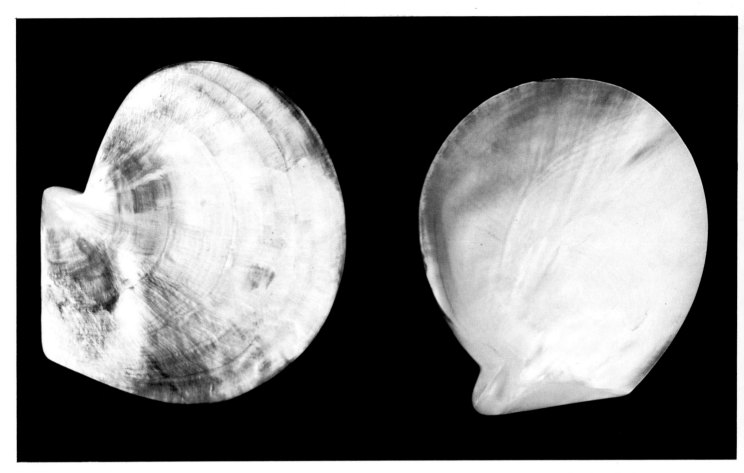

occur when the intrusive particle lodges between the mantle and the shell and the pearl becomes attached to the shell, growing into a half-sphere. Such pearls are known as blister pearls. Most blister pearls are sorted out of the pearl shell valves by the shell dealers, but every so often a sorter makes a mistake and a blister pearl goes on the market. If first drilled around and then tapped out of the parent valve a blister pearl may prove to be valuable—sometimes fully shaped pearls are enclosed in this same way—but it may also turn out to be misshapen, hollow, or a black liquid mass and entirely worthless.

Well-shaped pearls are formed when the irritant penetrates sufficiently deeply into the mantle or other soft tissue of the mollusk for the sac of tissue that forms around it to form a pouch shape and to close itself at the neck. If positioned so that there is no unequal pressure upon it, the pearl will form into a spherical or a pear shape, but if pressure or solid tissue prevent it forming symmetrically the pearl will be deformed. Oddly shaped pearls are known as baroque pearls and were once much sought after by jewelers. This was particularly the case during the Renaissance, when the jewelers would invest the shape with the character of an animal or the body of a hero or a god and incorporate it into an elaborate design.

The pearl owes its radiance to the phenomenon known as iridescence, produced by the way in which the material is deposited. Aragonite, the terrestrial twin of nacre, has an exactly similar chemical and molecular content, but no iridescence at all. The crinkled mantle of the shell deposits a wrinkled layer, laid on in ridge after ridge like a miniature mountain range. The *lamellae* or plates making up this layer show both their faces and their edges to the light. This breaks up the rays of sunshine, splitting the white light into the separate colors of the spectrum, just as would a glass prism or a cobweb covered by dewdrops.

Many people are surprised when they are told that cameos are really cut from shell. They imagine that this attractive jewelry is cut from some hard gemstone. They are usually even more surprised when I tell them that the cameo shells cost about $1.25 to buy, and that without expensive lapidary equipment, but with just a few simple steel tools, they can proceed to cut cameos for themselves. Finished cameos may cost $50.00 or more, but

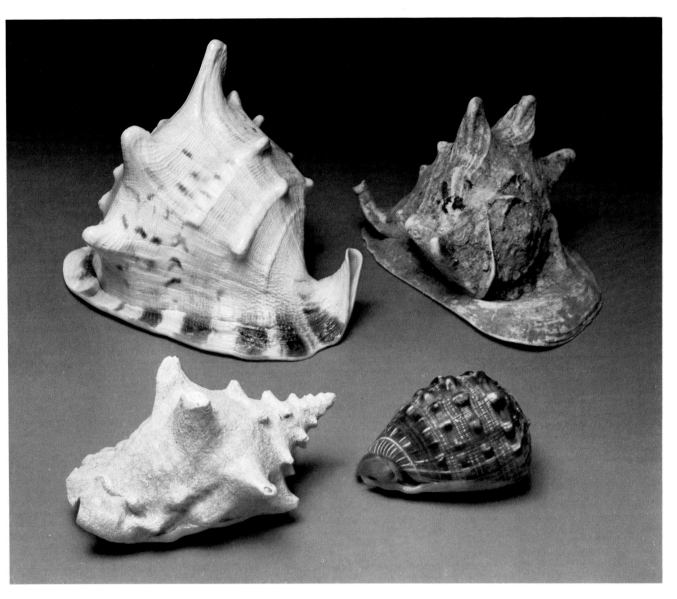

The pearl seen in all its glory in a modern setting.

A Victorian papier-mâché chair with an elaborate inlay of mother-of-pearl.

of course in a finished cameo cut by an artist you are paying for skill, skill that has accumulated over hundreds of years, ever since the cameo carvers began work in Italy in the 15th century. At Torre del Greco, a suburb of Naples, they are still at work. The artist gets his uncut cameos as blanks, small pieces of shell cut from a large helmet shell with a lapidary's saw. He sticks them to a dop stick with a mixture of melted wax and resin, fixes the stick in a vice and with a pencil draws a head, or whatever subject he wishes to carve, on the surface of the blank. Now he files round the outside of this head with a steel file till he has cut away the upper layer of the shell to give him the ground color. This is a different color from the middle layer of the shell, in which the head is carved. With just a few square, rounded or triangular-shaped gravers he cuts out the head, afterwards polishing the cameo with pieces of pumice stone, and finely powdered pumice rubbed on with a piece of limewood.

The first cameos were cut in Renaissance times from cowries, but nowadays all cameos come from helmet shells, principally the bull mouth *(Cassis rufa)*, which has a tawny-red ground, the king helmet *(Cassis tuberosa)* which has a brown ground, the black helmet *(Cassis madagascarenis,* which despite its name, does not come from Madagascar), with a beautiful chocolate ground, and the queen conch *(Strombus gigas)*, which has a delicate pink ground color.

The Lore of Shells

THROUGHOUT the centuries the shell has held an important position in the world's religions. This probably had its origin in the resemblance between the underside of a cowrie shell and the human female sexual organ. The earliest of the world's religions were closely linked with the idea of fertility and the need for regeneration. Fertility was the mystery of life itself, and to the men of antiquity there could be no more effective amulet against the powers of darkness than a fertility symbol.

The shape of the cowrie was copied in every kind of material from Phoenician times onwards. As late as the 17th century Spanish craftsmen were still carving clenched fists, the fingers held towards the viewer. This clenched fist was a symbol of a symbol, a representation of the cowrie. Once established, the connection

between shells and sexuality has never been broken. Venus is supposed to have risen in a shell, from the waves, off the island of Cyprus.

In ancient India, another kind of shell, the sacred chank, claimed the gods' attention. It was an attribute of the gods Siva, Vishnu and Krishna. Vishnu overcame a giant chank named "Shankhasura," who had stolen the books of sacred writings, and Krishna, one of Vishnu's incarnations, also destroyed a demon who lived in a giant chank shell.

Libations were poured from conches and, turned upside down, they served as lamps to light the temple. "May this conch, universal remedy," runs a Brahmin hymn, "save us from danger." Chanks which spiraled to the right were especially sacred. Shells of this sort were blown by the priests only on special occasions and then only for those wealthy votaries who could afford to pay heavily for this privilege. Perhaps the strangest use of the chank in religion was the fashioning from it of bracelets which took the place, among orthodox Hindu ladies, of the wedding ring among ourselves. A well-brought-up Hindu girl would retain her virginity until she was wearing several chank bracelets.

At the other side of the globe, in ancient Mexico, where Quetzalcoatl, the White God of the Aztecs, lived in four palaces made from shells of different colors and sat upon a shell throne, it is not surprising to find that the shell entered deeply into religious affairs. It is laid in the grave with the dead and it serves to ornament the Faces of the Gods—mosaic masks placed over the statues of the deities, or on the faces of dead kings.

There seems to have been no land, and no age, in which shells were not venerated in one way or another. In ancient Phoenicia, the insignia of the venerable and the royal was a dye, the famous Tyrian purple, made from a mollusk. The straight spined murex *(Bolinus brandaris)* and the banded murex *(Hexaplex trunculus)* were the usual species used. The shells and their occupants were thrown into stone pits and macerated to release the pigment which is secreted on the lower surface of the mantle between the intestines and the respiratory organs in a kind of band. The coloring matter was removed as a golden yellow fluid. Once exposed to the light, it becomes first green, then purple.

It was this color that dyed the borders of the togas of Roman senators and the mantles of kings: the "royal purple." The word came to be used for a scarlet red, and is found in many references with this meaning–perhaps because the color did not always dye true, though certainly its stain was very permanent. Dye from the murex runs like a thread of purple through the whole of the New Testament from the Lydia mentioned in ACTS 14.16 as a dyer of purple cloth, to the scarlet robe, emblem of royalty, in which Christ was clothed before his crucifixion.

Other shells provided somewhat less brilliant purples outside the Mediterranean. The Britons extracted their dye from the dog whelk *(Nucella lapillus)* and on the Pacific coast of Central America and northern South America the *Purpura patula pansa* was used in prehistoric times and still provides a dye used by the Tehuantepec Indians.

The royal purple was worn by the princes of the Church as well as secular kings and is the color of the altar cloth for the celebration of Christ's Passion.

Perhaps the greatest role played by shells in religion came during the Middle Ages, when the scallop, or pecten shell *(Pecten Jacobus)*, was adopted as the badge of the pilgrim, particularly the pilgrim to the shrine of St. James of Compostela, whose name is recalled in the scientific name of the scallop.

The famous palace in Salamanca, Spain, ornamented with beautifully carved scallop shells.

63

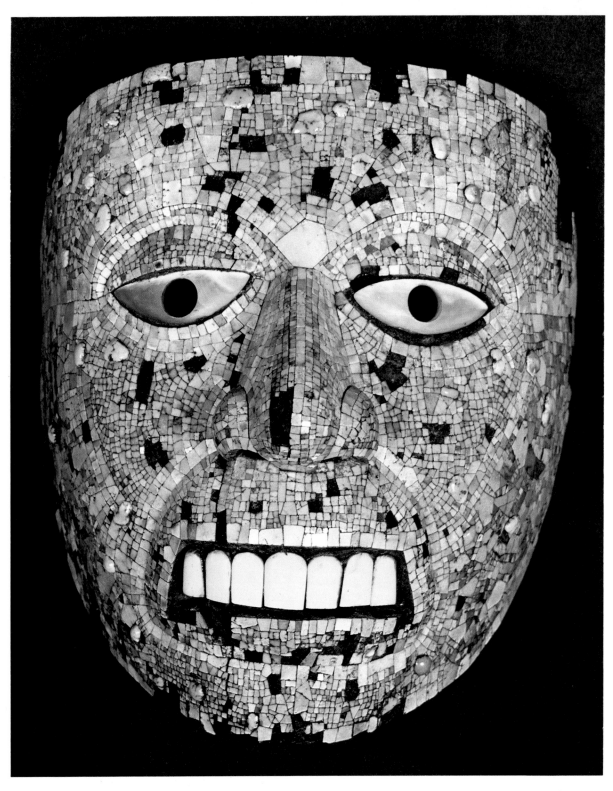

How did St. James of Spain obtain his scallop? It is at least possible that the old, amuletic associations attached to the cowrie had transferred, by medieval times, to other shells. At any rate, if anyone sewed a cockle shell in his hat, and set out, everyone knew he was a pilgrim, and would give him hospitality.

Perhaps in commemoration of a pilgrimage the scallop shell was often used as a charge in heraldic blazons. It now figures on many coats-of-arms of the oldest families, notably on that of the Duke of Montrose.

Above *The turquoise mask of Quetzalcoatl, the Aztec god of learning, with eyes and teeth of white shell.*

Right *Shellfish have always been, and still are, a valued culinary delicacy.*

Shellfish as Food

MANKIND might never have survived the first few million years of existence were it not for the abundant food supply offered by the seashore. In parts of the world as far apart as Denmark and Japan, great banks of empty shells have been discovered, the kitchen middens on which prehistoric man threw his leavings. He was so fond of eating shellfish that for hundreds of years he ate scarcely anything else. Shell mounds found at Omari in Japan measured twenty feet in depth in places. They were discovered, appropriately enough, not by an archaeologist, but a marine biologist, Edward S. Morse, who went to Japan in the late 19th century to start the first scientific marine studies there. Scientists estimate that it must have taken half a millennium to build up a bed of this thickness.

Once having discovered the palatability of so many mollusks, man made them a habit. By Roman times people were already spending fortunes on fish dinners. Britain, then a remote and almost legendary country, became known to the Romans when they heard about its pearls–and its oysters. Roman oyster shells, nicked with the four-sided knife seafood gourmets used in those days to open the mollusk, have been found in the debris of ancient towns of Roman Britain such as Colchester, where oysters are still fished.

A seafood stall at Littlehampton, England, in the early years of the century.

Modern processing, cold storage and new methods of distribution have done a great deal to bring down the price of the oyster. Nevertheless cockles and mussels, along with winkles, have taken its place as the poor man's seafood. New hope dawns for the oyster lover in the development of a new breed of oyster that will be equally good all the year round: oysters are scarcest, and not at their best, during the summer months when they are breeding.

In America eating shellfish is not just a gastronomic occasion, it is a social one as well. The Clambake and Oyster Roast are American traditions which probably date back to Pilgrim times. A gay picnic crowd will assemble on the beach and search out clams by digging up the sand at high tide. All sorts of tools have been evolved for this purpose, and in Canada a long-toothed rake is used. One very objectionable Canadian Indian chief was finally disposed of when one of his wives trapped him with just such a clam rake as he lay in bed, while the others finished him off. When a suf-

ficient quantity of clams have been collected, they are piled onto a heap of driftwood and baked in the hot ashes of the bonfire. Nothing is so delicious as a freshly baked clam or oyster, eaten in the open air.

Other American seafood delicacies include the abalone, which has now been placed under restrictive regulations by conservation authorities, coquina clams, which make delightful chowder, and scallops. It is difficult to think of anything that could delight the gourmet more than boiled savory scallops with just the right amount of Worcestershire sauce, curry powder, lime juice, and paprika.

One of the most famous of all shellfish dishes is clam chowder. To make it, according to Herman Melville, you take: "small juicy clams, scarcely bigger than hazel nuts, mixed with pounded ship biscuit, and salted pork cut up into little flakes; the whole enriched with butter and plentifully seasoned with pepper and salt."

With so many delicious American oysters

and clams available Americans have tended to neglect many of the humbler seafoods, eaten in "Old England," but left strictly for the birds on New England beaches. These lesser shellfish include periwinkles and whelks. In Britain they are boiled, and served up with their shells.

Paella is the Spanish national dish. It consists of rice fried in butter, to which is added mussels, saffron, lobster and other ingredients. Nowhere are mariscos (seafood) consumed with more religious zeal than in Spain.

Bouillabaisse is a characteristic dish of the Marseilles area. A fish bisque is made from several kinds of fish, with shellfish sometimes added to the soup, and sometimes served on the half shell.

Many more mollusks would provide good eating than are actually eaten in Western Europe and America. The range of shellfish eaten by the Japanese, and even particular parts of France, is immense and shows how far we might go in the future in using mollusks to provide proteins for a hungry world.

Shell Collecting and Display

LIKE decorative minerals, shells have become the favorites of people at large, rather than the prerogative of just a few natural scientists. I suspect that many more people now collect shells for their color, and for their unusual shapes, than because they are particularly interested in malacology. This is as it should be. It is not given to everyone to become a dedicated biologist.

It would be a pity to neglect the aesthetic appeal of shells. People should collect objects they like. If they like beautiful shells, then their collection should be based on aesthetic charm rather than malacological completeness.

However, I do not personally believe that one ought to neglect the scientific side of shell life entirely and concentrate purely on color and shape. It helps to have a basic grounding in malacology. It is only by knowing something about the background to conchology that you can talk fruitfully to other collectors, use text-

Below. *On the right,* Mitra vittata, *a rare shell from the Philippines, and on the left, the delicately shaped* Latiaxis deburghiae *from* Japan. Latiaxis *was once very rare, and is still highly prized for its beauty.*

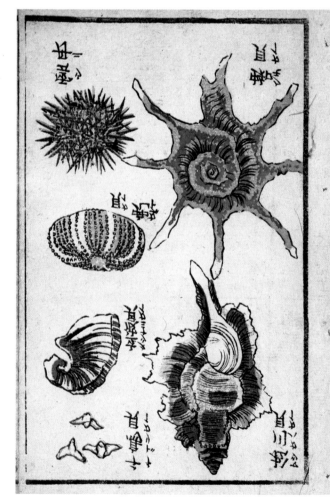

Above *The imperial volute (*Voluta imperialis*), a rare and beautiful collector's item, and (right), a page from a Japanese shell-collectors' handbook.*

Right *John Tradescant, the 17th-century British collector, showing his collection to a friend.*

Top left *The Scaphella junonia, a rare shell from Florida.*

Bottom left *A natural history collection of the 18th century, including a display of shells.*

books intelligently, work out a logical method of cataloging your collection, or even realize the ambition of every shell collector and discover a completely new shell.

Another side to shell collecting, which is not always stressed by books on the subject, is the romantic, exotic appeal of shells. To collect shells is to travel by proxy. It is not difficult to set out on a mantelpiece of an ordinary apartment enough shells to carry you, in imagination, right around the world. Shells speak to us of lands which we have never visited. Just by holding shells in our hands, these countries seem nearer; we almost feel we have seen them, and heard the sea crashing on their beaches.

If you are attracted to far-off places and exotic shells because you feel that there is a frustrated beachcomber in you, concentrate on tropical shells and leave the native varieties to those who are interested in them.

Of course it pays to beachcomb yourself. No way of acquiring shells is more interesting than collecting them in the field, or rather, on the shore. An inspired collector like the late Ian Fleming would never buy shells from professional gatherers; he preferred the specimens he had found for himself. Every item in his collection was, for him, a personal triumph.

Every collecting trip should be planned well beforehand. Obtain a map of the collecting area; mark on it the parts of the coast likely to be fruitful in shells. The biological department of your local university or other large college is likely to be of great help to you here in giving you information as to where to collect. If you have time to spend in the area, visit the local museum, or the local natural history society, and see what the collections there are like. Acquire local information by chatting to fishermen and other folk who know the seashore, such as coastguards and lighthousemen. Fishermen who use nets inevitably bring up lots of shells that are of no use to them; ask them to keep some for you.

The best time to visit the beach is at low tide, or perhaps an hour beforehand. Ask the usual commonsense questions about the times of tides, whether there are quicksands and on what days of the month the very high and low tides fall.

Unless you have it in mind to dig for burrowing lamellibranchs, do not waste time on sandy beaches; go for rocky coasts with lots of rock pools and boulders that can be upturned. Scrambling over rocks is best undertaken in old clothes, and rope-soled or rubber-soled shoes that will not slip on wet rocks. If you are going to do a lot of walking along the bottom of pools, have an old pair punched with holes just above the sole so that the water can run out of them.

Collecting equipment should be kept to the minimum. I recommend a knapsack to carry everything you need, a crowbar, the hooked end of which can be dragged under the overhang of rock pools, while the other end will be useful for overturning boulders. Plastic garbage bags on a roll are useful for wrapping large specimens, such as dog whelks while small plastic tubes used for medicine are suitable for small ones. A small hand net, such as a shrimping net, is handy for dragging through weeds, and for collecting crustacea,

"Pegwell Bay" by William Dyce shows a Victorian family engaged in the fashionable pastime of shell collecting.

whose backs often harbor mollusks. Carry a pocket magnifying glass and a notebook and pencil, kept in a waterproof plastic case, which will be useful for logging specimens. Do not forget to add the map reference so that you can go back again to a productive area.

Collect in a way that will favor conservation. Examine everything likely to be productive of shells—jetties, gores, piers, pieces of timber, rocks and sand. But do not deplete small colonies, take too many specimens, collect young shells, or fail to replace anything you turn over.

You can collect live specimens in a pailful of sea water, take them back home and keep them in an aquarium until they die a natural death. Then, instead of boiling them alive you may learn a good deal about living shellfish. To remove them from their shells you must drop them in boiling water in a special saucepan kept for this purpose. Remove the body of the animal with a stout hook such as a crochet hook. Wash the shells thoroughly with liquid detergent and hot water, using an old toothbrush to scrub them. Dry them thoroughly and rub them with a chamois. Eighteenth-century col-

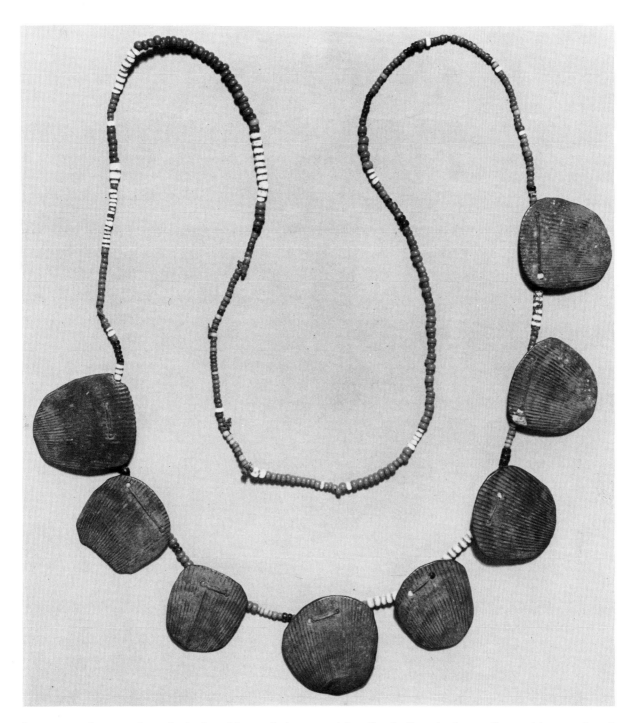

lectors used a woolen cloth for this, to bring up the gloss on the surface of the shell. A little good-quality wax polish will help to bring out the surface pattern and polish of the shell. You may decide that you want to strip away the outside of a shell so as to display the iridescent layer. Seventeenth-century collectors used to do this. Do not use acid; this will merely deteriorate the nacre and make it look yellow. Grind off the periostracum, using a grindstone fitted to an electric drill. For most shells, the periostracum is quite thin. If you want to polish the nacre, on the outer or inner side of a shell, rub the surface with powdered pumice and water, then powdered tripoli and water, or putty powder, put on with a wet cotton rag. Finish with a rag dipped in a mild solution of copper sulphate dissolved in water.

Label each shell and number it. You can label it with a very unobtrusive number if you use as ink a little thinned enamel paint applied with a mapping pen. Alternatively write a number in India ink, which will not fade, on an adhesive sticker and attach it to the shell. Once more, the number need not be obvious. Put it on the inside of the lip for instance. Keep a catalog of all the shells you collect, listing the type of shell, where collected, and when.

No matter how far traveled a collector may be, he may want to buy shells as well as collect them. Air travel, with its baggage limits, will only permit him to bring back a few of the specimens he would like to possess. Furthermore, buying shells is fun. They are very cheap, as collectors' items go.

A browse through the yellow pages of your local telephone directory will tell you where the nearest shell shop is. Many can be found in the big cities; several are listed on page 79.

The ultimate in shell buying is a visit to the big auction sales where specimens, many of them collected many years ago when there were more shells to pick and choose from, come under the ivory hammer. Dealers get many of their shells in the big sales, so the auction price of a shell is bound to be less than the dealer's price.

If you cannot obtain a shell you particularly want in this country, try writing to a shop in its country of origin. You should be able to obtain a list of the country's shell dealers from their Embassy. Try to write in the language of the country concerned; if not, write in English. Enclose a sketch of the shell you want as well as its conchological name so as to avoid misunderstanding.

Everyone ought to take the greatest care of his treasures. The collection of live shells will soon be banned, just as bird's egg collecting is at present. America has already shown the way in which things are going by putting restrictions on the collection of abalones, so that soon only already existing collections will be available for study.

If you have many large specimens, keep them in individual cardboard boxes. You can order standard sets of these in several sizes from cardboard box manufacturers. Line these with contrasting colored paper, and use standard labels to identify them. You can have a set printed at no great cost. Type out the entries for the labels on a justifying typewriter with a bookface type, or label them boldly in clear calligraphic script. Keep smaller shells in wood cabinets with shallow drawers. Cabinets

Shell collecting on the Great Barrier Reef, Australia.

"The Conchologists," a drawing poking gentle fun at the 18th-century enthusiasm for natural history.

*A fine shell arrangement in the form of a
flowerpiece, showing a variety of common shells
to their best possible advantage.*

of this sort can be bought very cheaply in whitewood, and then stained. You can arrange partitions for the drawers, made from stout cardboard covered with burlap, or some other stick-on fabric, which will enable you to keep many tiny shells in one drawer.

It is one thing to arrange and catalog shells, it is another to set them out so as to get the full aesthetic value from your collection. Every shell collector, however, would agree that shells make wonderful decorative elements. It is merely a question of deciding how best they can show off their good points.

Glass shelving and glass-topped tables are excellent for displaying shells, but if you place them on highly polished furniture remember that shells often have rough bases or sharp corners and may scratch it. If you are displaying an assortment of shells, set each on an individual mat. Fortunately shell shops usually sell straw mats as well.

Arrange pyramids or piles of shells in the way in which Tradescant and other Baroque collectors used to display their treasures. Pile them in a large antique china bowl, or a silver

tray. An arrangement of small shells under a glass dome, of the kind the Victorians used to house wax fruit, is also very striking. Combine the shells with a few well-arranged fronds of dried seaweed, coral, sea urchins and other marine treasures.

Individual shells can be placed in display boxes. These can often be contrived from the kind of transparent box in which food is sold, or from a clear plastic sandwich box. A wooden base can be made from some decorative wood, such as mahogany, and lined underneath with felt, so that the shell can be placed on polished furniture. Shadow boxes, or nests of interlocking wooden shelves hung on the wall, are a good means of displaying shells. If you have a particularly decorative tall shell, put it in one of the boxes you can buy in Chinese shops. They are covered with brocade outside, have a glass front panel, and are lined with silk inside. The shell can be placed in this and the box stood upright.

A display of shells on a mantelpiece will be enhanced by an appropriate picture hung nearby. One made from pressed and dried

Detail of a page from a 19th-century treatise on conchology.

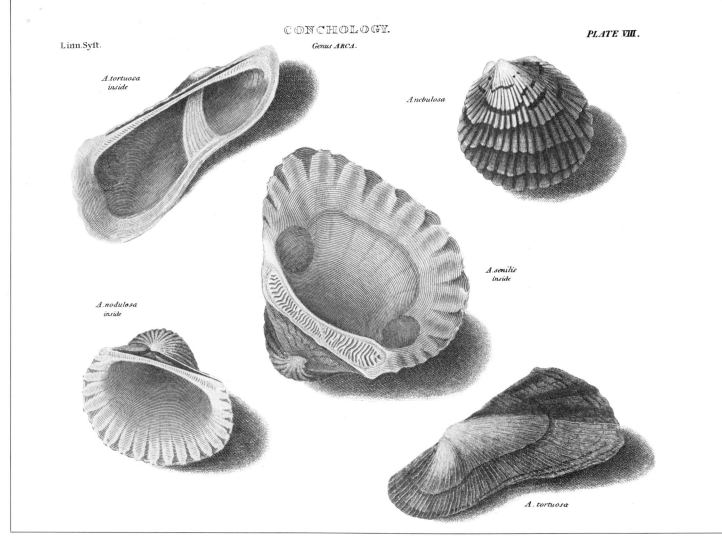

Linn.Syft.

Genus ARCA.

A.tortuosa inside

A.nodulosa inside

Anchulosa

A.senilis inside

A. tortuosa

seaweed perhaps, or a print of shells from an old encyclopedia. Extremely effective are 18th-century engravings which incorporate shells as decoration (the 18th century was the age of decorative elements based on shells). An engraving of the seaside, or a framed poem about shells, also make admirable foils for a display of shells.

You will probably acquire many duplicate shells which you do not want to exchange, or sell. You may like to make a shell picture from some of those.

In pet shops and supermarkets you can buy sheets of sandpaper for birdcages. Buy a sheet of this paper and glue it down on a sheet of hardboard large enough to give you a margin of an inch or so all round.

Select one or two decorative pebbles, not too many or too large, and tumble-polish them, or hand-polish them. If you do not have the necessary lapidary equipment you can simply varnish them with any clear var-

nish. Stick them down on the sandpaper sheet, using cold-water glue. Select some dried natural seaweed, not the thick fleshy kind but the thin fronded variety, or use decorative foliage, which you can buy. Do not attach too much of this to the picture; just a spray or so will be sufficient.

Now choose a few decorative shells, and position them on the sandpaper so that they will look as attractive as possible. Stick them down with cold-water glue. This will make a good bond, yet if you want to remove the shells afterwards you can pull them off and then scrape away all the glue from them. Virtually all shells are harder than the edge of a steel blade. You should be able to scrape off the glue without harming the surface of the shell, but experiment first with shells that are expendable.

Inspiration, and constant observation of museum exhibits and shell shop windows, will suggest many new ideas to you.

Customers inspecting the merchandise in a shell shop in London.

Selected Retail Shell Shops

The Collector's Cabinet
1000 Madison Avenue
New York, NY 10021

King's Seashell and Rock Shop
12 Guild Street
Norwood
Massachusetts 02062

Elsie Malone Shell Shop
Sanibel Island
Florida 33957

Moon's
301 West Main Street
Twin Falls
Idaho 83301

Nautilus Arts & Crafts
6515 Kingston Road
West Hill
Ontario, Canada

Nautilus Gift Shop
Box 204
Virginia Beach
Virginia 23458

Paradise Shells
2126 Kalakaua Avenue
Honolulu, Hawaii
HI 96815

Seashells Unlimited Inc.
590 Third Avenue
New York, NY 10016

Shells of the Seas Inc.
PO Box 1418
Fort Lauderdale
Florida 33302

Trails End Crafts
Route 4, Box 25
Huntsville
Arkansas 72740

West Coast Curio Co.
1940 Maple Avenue
Costa Mesa
California 92627

Western Australian Shells
Box T 1738
GPO Perth
West Australia 6001

Wheeler's Rocks and Shells
Highway 89
Elsinore, Utah 84724

Young's Rock Shop
3133 Euclid Avenue
Bay City
Michigan 48706

*An elegant arrangement of neutral-colored
shells under a glass dome.*